WISDOMS

By Bobby Glen James

8 WISDOMS

Copyright © 2012 by Bobby Glen James

Book Website
www.8Wisdoms.com
Email: contact@8wisdoms.com
Give feedback on the book at:
feedback@8wisdoms.com

8Wisdoms Forum
www.8Wisdoms.net

8Wisdoms
www.8wisdoms.org

Printed in U.S.A

CHARTER LIGHT
PUBLISHING
www.CharterLight.com

8
WISDOMS

By
Bobby Glen James

LAND OF

City of Tal

The Temple

Temple City

The Great Desert

Cachy Mountains

City of Ivicas

THE MASTER

Prison

Helain Mountains

City of Hiin

Old Man Chu Farm

Master's Palace

Momotha River

City of Chee

City of Bahe

N

Dedication

To Robert and Delores, who have been my greatest supporters throughout my life. They were instrumental in creating the person I am, showing me I could do or be anything in this world. Also to my wife, Monique, who has been one of the strongest influences in my life; without her I am only half a man. To my kids, Laijun, Jathun, and Chay, who love the bedtime stories we make up together.

The Alchemist

A force appears to be negative, but actually shows you how to realize your Personal Legend. It prepares your spirit and your will, because there is one great truth on this planet: whoever you are, or whatever it is that you do, when you really want something, it is because that desire originated in the Soul of the Universe. It is your mission on earth.

Paulo Coelho

Prologue

The boy bled from cuts and scratches. Tree branches and brush tore his tattered clothing; tears run down his dirty face, leaving streaks of grime and blood. He had been running for what seemed an eternity. Life in the village he had known was gone. The faces of his family faded, replaced by an evil world.

All the boy loved and knew was gone. Why is life a lie? Soon he would pass out from exhaustion.

In the distance he saw a flickering flame. The light sent shock waves through his mind. Could this fire be the man he sought. The boy ran faster and faster to get to the fire.

Hatred possessed his mind. I will destroy him. He focused on avenging his lost loved ones.

As he got closer he could see that the fire was small. There was no evil leader or soldiers. The young boy's body gave way to fatigue.

He stopped.

A woman of considerable age, cooking a simple meal sat at the fire. That was all the boy saw before his body collapsed, sending him into a deep and dark unconsciousness.

The Journey Ends
Nightmares Remain

I had been traveling for a year with the Seeker's Map.

I was almost to the palace gate. I had been looking at the fortress for miles. A wall surrounded the palace as a shield. On the outside of the protective wall was a moat with a bridge crossing to the entrance. Guards scoured the landscape from the top of the wall. I reached a large gate, which was the entrance into enormous grounds. Two guards stood straight looking like statues created from marble.

I walked across the bridge where the sentries stood and the guard looked down at me with a frown on his face. "State your business."

"I have traveled a great distance to see the Master."

"Why do you seek the Master?" asked the guard as he looked down at me.

"A woman I lived with in the wilderness told me I should seek him."

The guard glared at me. "We were not expecting anyone. What is the name of this woman?"

"She called herself Lelolien, the Seeker. She told me to say that I am the Apprentice, the one the Master seeks." I was filthy and weary from the great journey. I could only guess how my appearance must look to these men.

"I have traveled a great distance to speak to the Master. Please let him know I am here."

The soldiers looked at each other with raised eyebrows. "All right, young man, the court gathering was finished yesterday. Do not expect too much. The Master is a busy man."

"I will wait," I said.

The smaller guard went through the gates. I stood, expecting a summons from the one called Master soon. Eventually the man came back. "The Master will see you, but you must wait."

Minutes went by, then hours. Night came, and I waited on a stone bench by the entrance. I was exhausted. I realized the Master would not see me this day. I sat on the bench dreading the night. I thought of my brother and sister, Patin and Keira. I think of them now with so much love in my heart. I felt sad knowing I could have been better to them and now it was too late. Life is such an evil worthless existence.

I remembered my brother Patin and how he always followed me and wanted to be with me and my friends. I was always annoyed with him. I thought he was just too young to be any fun. He looked up to me with unfailing love. How I wished I could tell him how much I loved him and appreciated the love he had shown me.

I thought of Keira, who was such a sweet little sister. She always wanted someone to play dolls with. I was a boy and did not want to play dolls but one day I gave in to her pleading. My doll wanted to fight and jump off cliffs into water, not drink sweet tea. How I wish I could play dolls with her again. Tears streamed down my cheeks as I pictured her soft beautiful face and that smile that captured my heart.

I pictured my father and me working in the fields getting the crops ready. How I'd hated it! I complained about why we had to work so hard. I would give anything to work beside my father now. He was so wise, a fair and gentle man. I always knew he loved mother more than life itself. I thought if I had the chance I would work hard in the field if only I could be with him again.

My mother was the strongest part of our family. She was the most spiritual and loving person but could be stern when she needed to be. I remember her rocking me as a child and her loving kisses and hugs. I also remember as I got older I did not want the hugs and kisses any more and would tell my mother I was too old for that show of affection. I knew I hurt her when I said those things. I would give anything to have the opportunity to be held and kissed again.

Life is not worth living. My family was my life. I cried as I did almost every night as I lay on the bench. I dreaded the nights and the nightmares that came with sleep.

As I slept, I dreamed.

I was happy as I lay in my small bed listening to dogs barking and the laughter of village children outside. How can anyone be happy and not appreciate the joy of the ordinary—until it is gone? My world had been perfect, my life full, every day I felt the same degree of happiness.

I listened for a while as my mother hummed her favorite song. The scent of flatbread and herbal tea permeated the small hut.

"Good morning sleepy-head," my mother said cheerfully. "After you have eaten, go to the village in the north and take one of the goats to the vendors market. Trade it for supplies."

I ate breakfast and got ready for my trip. I could feel my mother's love and trust for me.

The village was four hours away. It was much bigger than our small settlement. I was excited that my mother trusted me to travel alone. In the big village squar there was lots of trading. I saw sellers hawking their wares, each one different from the others. I saw delectable fruits, figs, nuts, rice, cloth—anything and everything was set up to please.

I spied a juggler and watched with the other people for a long while. What a great talent he had. I thought that someday, I would juggle like this man. I paused as I remembered the juggler, and then continued as I thought of the girls in the streets. I watched the girls dancing, admiring their beauty and thinking how much my point of view had changed in the past year.

I noticed the sun in the afternoon sky. I traded the goat, got the needed supplies, and walked out of the village. The sun felt warm on my face. I fantasized about how I would look as a juggler. People would smile as they watched my talent in awe.

After several hours, as the sun started its downward descent, I saw smoke in the sky in the distance. As I got closer, I saw a hut on fire! Fear began to creep up my spine. I dropped the supplies and ran as fast as I could. Terror raced through my mind. The smoke burned my eyes and lungs. I could barely see or breathe.

Men were slashing every villager: men, women, children—it did not matter. Women and children were screaming in terror. Death and destruction reigned from one end of the village to the other.

I paused at the horror before me. I found my family in front of our humble home. My father's body lay over my mother's to shield her. Close by lay little Patin and Keira. In disbelief I slumped to the ground. I could do nothing but wait for my own death. An assassin walked toward me.

An enormous man lifted his sword to strike me. I looked up and met the black eyes of a horseman just behind the swardsman. I could see years of destruction and torment. We locked eyes for what seemed an eternity. Hate for this man boiled in my heart as I looked into his dark soul. I was ready for death.

Still peering into my eyes, the man on the horse yelled, "Stop – Let the boy live!" The executioner cowered at the sound of his voice.

"Yes, Master Udoki," the grunt warrior said as he lowered his sword.

The name Udoki burned into my brain. It returned over and over again in my dream, "Udoki."

I vowed at that moment that my only reason for living was to kill him.

After destroying our settlement, the men disappeared. I was motionless for some time. I crawled to my family and checked them for any sign of life. If only I could bring them back.

All I could do was fixate about the warlord with the dead black eyes and seek revenge. I ran faster to rid my mind of the memory as my body started to give way.

Run! Run! Run!

I jumped from the hard stone bench and did all I could to catch my breath. I laid back down, drifting in and out of sleep.

Next morning, aching from the hard bench. I realized I was hungry to the point of starvation.

The guards looked at me and one shouted. "Go into the guard house kitchen and get some food." He pointed to a small shack just inside the gates.

I shrugged my shoulders and nodded. I was too hungry to spend another day and night on the cold bench.

The guard said, "Go to the shack, ask Mehi for some food, and clean yourself up."

I found the kitchen where fresh cooked bread had been prepared and was on the table. The woman called Mehi had baked a large loaf of hot bread. It was right out of the oven and she added a jar of fresh honey. There was a jug of water in the middle of the table.

The woman looked me up and down.

I asked, "May I have something to eat? The guards told me to ask for food?"

She nodded her head.

I ate the mouth-watering hot bread and honey, then drank cool water. Every drop filled the dry emptiness within me.

She crooked her finger, indicating the cleaning bowl on the shelf. "Clean the dirt and blood off, then let's see what you look like." She smiled, looking at the shreds of what used to be my clothing.

"My boy's about your size. I'll find you some proper clothing." She pointed to a shelf and said, "Soap's right up there."

I had forgotten how good soap and water felt. As I finished cleaning myself I could see mud floating in the bowl. I put on the clothes that Mehi laid out for me. The pants cuffs piled on the floor and the uncomfortable shirt-sleeves hung at least a foot from my hands.

He must be a big boy, I thought. I laughed at the way I looked.

After I was full and had finished eating, I returned to the cold bench to wait.

The sun was beginning its descent for the day. "Did the Master forget about me?" I yelled at the guards.

"Master knows you are here and will see you when he is ready," replied one of the guards.

The second day passed and I waited. The third day came and I was getting weary. On the fourth day, I thought I would move on.

I looked at the guards in anger, "I am going to leave. This is pointless. It is obvious the Master does not want to see me."

"Four days is a short time for someone who has traveled so far," the guard said.

I pondered over the guard's words and decided to wait until I was asked to leave, or until the Master summoned me. I had nowhere to go; but I still grew impatient. I decided this place was as good as any. Mehi's food was abundant and I did not go hungry.

"I will wait," I yelled to the guards.

The fifth day arrived and I began to wonder if Lelolien's message was really for me. Maybe she was wrong. Perhaps I was not the one the Master sought.

A woman came to the guards and spoke to them. One of the guards looked at me and said, "The Master will see you now."

I followed the messenger through the entrance. I was surprised at the splendor I saw. Inside was a decorated courtyard. The surroundings contained many colors of flat stones. I thought that it must have taken years to build such beautiful grounds, with each rock chiseled by hand to a smooth surface. As we walked up the stairs, I could see the red pillars. We stopped before two massive gold doors. I had never seen anything so striking. My heart raced as I realized I was finally going to see the Master.

The Master

The messenger opened the door and bid me enter. I peered around the messenger.

"Come," said a soft voice. There was something magical about this man as he sat on a beautiful straight-backed chair. I stood mesmerized by the power that came from his presence. He had an ancient face of all knowing and long white hair flowing down behind his back.

The Master beckoned me to him. "You waited some time to see me. I see that your resolve is strong. How can I be of service to such a fine young man?" His blue eyes twinkled like stars.

"What quest brings you such a great distance?" What clouds your life to make you so serious? Your eyes look as though you are an ancient man rather than a young boy."

I paused, gathering my thoughts, but found it difficult to speak, now that I stood before the Master. "Go on," he said, gesturing me to come closer. "What brings you before me?"

I gradually began to tell the Master my story. A warlord named Udoki and his band of outlaws murdered my family. They took away my life—my world. I was the only one left alive. I ran through the wilderness wanting to find and destroy them.

Why

I would have died in the wilds but I found myself at the fire of Lelolien, the Seeker. I was close to death as I fell before her feet.

When I awoke, Lelolien was kind and nursed me back to health. As I lay there unable to move, she held me and wiped my forehead. I could not talk or respond. She fed me small pieces of bread and sips of water. As my health began to improve, I started talking. I told her my name was Shinhon and recounted what had happened. I told her my only desire in life was to destroy that man, Udoki.

I asked her, "Why is this world so bad, so full of such evil and destruction?"

Her voice was soft as she explained, "Life is about learning. We don't always know why things happen. Some things change our lives forever, but there are no accidents. Everything happens for a purpose."

She told me of a powerful and wise leader who was a ruler in a land far away to the west. She said she had been given the task as the Seeker to find one person to be his apprentice. She believed that I was that person. She told me he would answer my questions about the world. I was told to come here and tell you that Lelolien, the Seeker, had sent me to be your apprentice.

I looked into the blue twinkling eyes of the Master and said, "I have come to you for an answer to my questions. Why is this life so full of evil and sadness? What is the purpose of this life? Are we here only to endure the wickedness of this world?"

Quest for the Eight Wisdoms

The Master began to speak, "Lelolien sent you? I have great respect for her and I know that she only sends those that are ready to be taught. We shall see how you show up and what effort you will put forth to obtain that which you seek. Nothing is by pure chance or accident. There are divine reasons for good and evil in life. I will assist you in finding the answers to your questions. You have proven your determination by making this journey and waiting to see me, but you must be willing to go further. You are no longer a boy, and not yet a man. The lessons to fulfill your destiny are difficult. If you are willing and patient, you will have the answers. In life, many live at the whims of the winds of circumstance and let life move them from lesson to lesson without clear focus."

_The Master looked at me with kind ancient eyes.

"A man with wisdom is often described as a wise person. There are those in life who would say: There is a knowledgeable man, he is wise."

The Master moved closer, leaning forward in his chair. "Shinhon, wisdom requires more than knowledge. You must also have awareness. Many have great knowledge but do not live that knowledge, and that is not wisdom.

"I thought knowledge and wisdom were the same," I said.

The Master continued. "Wisdom is the open connection that makes it possible to comprehend the secrets of life. When the Eight Wisdoms are mastered you will possess full awareness. Then you will control your life like the captain of a ship. No longer will you be at the mercy of the sea of life."

The Master stopped speaking. He looked at me as if he was contemplating my reaction to his next words. "Shinhon, if you commit to me to learn and live the Eight Wisdoms of life, I will assist you in finding this man Udoki and whatever justice you feel necessary."

My heart jumped at the thought of the Master's help to destroy Udoki.

The Master continued, "I must have your promise as a student of the Eight Wisdoms that you will do your best to learn and become one with them. Swear that you will do all in your power to learn the wisdoms. Your training will begin tomorrow."

I replied with excitement, "Master, on my life, I make a solemn promise, to study and learn the Eight Wisdoms, whatever they may be."

I was shaking with exhilaration as I realized that, with this man's help, I could revenge my family and our village.

The Master spoke. "The Eight Wisdoms of life are simple but profound. Most people in this world never comprehend the Wisdoms. They go through life on a ship without a rudder or compass. Each Wisdom contains an awareness that connects to knowledge; Wisdom comes when it changes from something you know and becomes what you are. Being wise and knowledgeable is not the same. Knowledge without action is the same as a shelved hammer—useless."

Comprehending what the Master meant, I said, "It does you no good to own it unless you use it."

The Master nodded in agreement. "Tomorrow you will come before me. I will give you a task. After the task is completed I want you to return to me and explain what you have learned."

The Master looked at me with eyes of enchantment. He leaned toward me and with a soft voice asked, "Are you ready to start your training?"

"I am, Master," I said. I was ready—ready for revenge and the death of the one called Udoki.

WISDOM

1

"If you always put limit on everything you do, physical or anything else, it will spread into your work and into your life. There are no limits. There are only plateaus, and you must not stay there, you must go beyond them."

BRUCE LEE

The Puzzle

The room in which I stayed that night was twice as big as my home in the village. The bed was comfortable. On the stand next to the bed was a bowl of fruit. I was tired and sore from sleeping on the cold bench.

No matter the comfort I felt in that soft bed the visions would not leave my mind. My dreams always included the warlord.

Then dawn came. The smell of herb tea and flatbread woke me, the scent was bittersweet. A reminder of the last meal my mother prepared for me and our last conversation together.

I ate and dressed.

Before long, there came a knock at the door.

Mehi said, "The Master has called for you. Please come with me."

I grabbed a last bite from the flatbread tray and followed Mehi.

Soon we were at the Master's door. Mehi knocked.

"Come," the Master spoke.

As I approached him, he smiled. "Did you sleep well, Shinhon? Were your accommodations suitable?"

"More than I could imagine Master."

There, on a small table next to the Master, lay a beautiful round sphere.

"Come closer, Shinhon." The Master pointed to the object.

The handcrafted wood was artistic. There were intricate designs in the sphere.

I wondered what a piece of wood could teach me.

As if reading my mind the Master said "This will assist you in learning the first wisdom."

I thought that I would finish the wisdom by the end of the day. It looked easy enough to comprehend the beauty of the object.

"What is the meaning of this Master?"

"You tell me."

"Master. . . I do not understand. I know nothing."

"Knowing is the false prize of life. Knowing is no good unless you use your knowledge."

The Master looked to the sphere beside him. "This is what you will do. This beside me is a puzzle."

A puzzle?

The Master tapped the wooden sphere with his hand and it shattered into thousands of pieces.

"You are to go to the west side of the palace. There you will work on the puzzle. You have one year to complete the task."

What? One year? I thought I could complete it in one day.

"If you complete the puzzle before the year ends, you will report what you have learned. You will want for nothing. All you will do is work on the puzzle.

"Are you ready to begin the first of your assignments?"

"Yes, Master."

Everything I Wanted

The Master clapped his hands together and two servants came from behind the tapestries on the left side of the great room. "Take care of my apprentice," he said. "Make sure he is comfortable and all his needs are met."

The two servants motioned for me to follow them. They led me down a long corridor. Statues and exquisite tapestries decorated the surroundings. We walked through the garden. I could smell the aroma of many different flowers.

They led me into a room with one small window.

As the months passed I wanted for nothing. A servant was at my call to serve me anything. I gorged myself on all manner of foods: candies, pastries, and meats. I never had such wondrous comforts. I did not lift a finger for anything.

The first month I worked hard on the puzzle, devoting all my time to it. I sat in my room in complete concentration.

No matter how hard I twisted the pieces of wood or placed the pieces of the puzzle, nothing fit. With each move, I hoped the shards would come together. After a month of twisting and turning, the wooden pieces began to fit around the edges. By the second month, I had put several pieces together.

I began to despise the puzzle. To console myself, I ate even more of the wonderful foods. I grew heavier by the week.

I fell into a dark despair.

I am not the Apprentice. Lelolien was wrong.

I was lost on how I could learn the wisdoms of life. I never left my room. It would be better to be dead and not to deal with this life.

I was over half finished with it.

One day a servant knocked on the door. "Go away!" I shouted, but the knock continued.

"What is it?" I asked.

"Your year ends today," a man said.

"Give me more time. I can do this, I have half the puzzle put together and with a little more time I can finish it."

"The Master has sent for you."

I walked with a slow pace to the Master, dreading every step, not wanting to face him.

I bowed my head in shame before him.

The Master looked me over, observing the puzzle remains on the tray in my hands.

"Shinhon, you look different than when you left. There is much more of you now." His bright blue eyes twinkled.

"I see that the puzzle is only partway finished. Have you learned anything from the experience?"

"I failed at the task and learned nothing from the puzzle."

The Master said nothing, only looked at me with his piercing eyes.

"I had anything I wanted for food and drink. I gorged myself on exotic meats, breads, and desserts.

"As you can see, I have gained much weight. The first month I was committed and did well with my work on the puzzle. As the days went by it began to get harder and harder for me to concentrate. I found it painful to look at the puzzle. I have learned that I am a failure."

"You have not finished the first life wisdom," said the Master.

"I wonder if the Seeker chose the right person for you."

The Master dismissed my whining, and walked down the stairs to me. Side by side we stood.

"You will be given one more year to finish the puzzle. I am sending you to another place rather than the palace. You are to go to the northeast part of my kingdom in the canyons. There is a small farm where you will assist the owner. His name is Chu. You will work on his farm and after finishing your work for the day, you are to work on the puzzle."

I was astonished. I am to work on this puzzle for another year plus work on a farm!

"It will take you a few days to get to the farm. When you have finished the puzzle, you may return to the palace."

He waved his hand and with one swipe, the puzzle was scattered.

I was stunned. Everything I had accomplished lay in pieces. I looked up at him; he could see the surprise on my face.

"If you are to learn you must start at the beginning. Go to the farm and return when you have learned the first of life's wisdoms."

I did not want to leave the palace.

The Master handed me a map with directions and a note to give to the farm.

Everything I Needed

The journey to the farm was not difficult, but it was hot. My body was not used to moving. I made several stops along the way to eat and rest.

When I arrived at the farmhouse, I was met by an unfriendly old man.

"Are you Chu the owner of this farm?"

"Yes" he said with little emotion.

I handed him the note from the Master.

The old man took the message and read it. He looked me up and down. He was a stern man and did not seem forgiving. He told me it was good I was there, and I was just in time to dig a new well because the old one was almost dry.

"You will begin digging a new one," said the old farmer.

"When?" I asked.

"Now" he said.

Before showing me to my room, the farmer handed me a short shovel to dig with and presented the spot where I should dig. I looked at the old shrivel-faced man, and I gave him a new name. From that time on I would call him Old Man Chu.

He said he would come back for me later. I dug for what seemed to be an eternity. Old Man Chu came back with some food and drink. The food did not taste good, just a little rice and some vegetables. I was hungry after all the digging. I gulped it down. I was used to rich foods and this was almost tasteless.

I have never worked so hard. When I first began digging the well, it was easy but not being used to hard physical labor I soon began sweating. My clothing was soaking wet. I was covered in dirt. Many times I had to stop and take deep breaths to keep from passing out. I knew that the year in the palace had made me soft. That first day I felt like I was going to die.

At the end of the day, I went into the farmhouse and sat at the dinner table to eat with Old Man Chu and his wife Tara. My arms burned from the pain of shoveling dirt all day, and my hands were blistered. All I wanted was to fall into bed.

The food was simple: no meat or pastries, only vegetables and some rice cooked with spices. I was starved and wolfed everything down.

There was not much talking. It was awkward for me. After dinner, we sat by the fireplace and mended clothing. After digging the well, my arms and hands were stiff and awkward. Tara put some kind of ointment on the many blisters and wrapped my hands in bandages. She was gentle but not sweet.

Then Old Man Chu and Tara sat in front of a small table with what looked like a game of some kind. The table consisted of a strange star shape. There were six points on the star and on each point was an arrangement of different colored marbles sunk in small holes. It looked like the object of the game was to choose a colored set of marbles and move them in the small holes, taking turns until you had filled up your opponents star point." You could jump the other marbles so if your strategy was good you would reach the other side more quickly.

Chu and Tara played the game three times, not really talking at all. I just sat at the fire wanting to sleep.

After the third game, Old Man Chu led me to a room with a mat on the floor. I put my things in the room and noticed the puzzle. I had carried the pieces in a bag to the farm. The bag sat on a tray in the room. I placed the puzzle in the corner and did not look at it again. I fell into a deep sleep and, for the first time in months, I did not wake that night with bad dreams.

The old man was up at dawn.

"Boy," he yelled.

"My name is Shinhon," I said in a drowsy achy slur. I could barely move my body.

"Get up," Old Man Chu said, "That hole will not dig itself."

"Please, not the hole. Please let me rest just this day."

The old man spoke, "If we rest on the farm, then we die. Crops will not come in, animals will not be fed, and everything dies."

"Not in just one day," I said.

"One day turns into two, then three—then everything is dead."

He was a fun uplifting person, I thought sarcastically.

That day, every shovel full of dirt was a nightmare. The hole got deeper.

Old Man Chu attached a pulley to the top of the well so I could fill and dump the dirt as the hole got deeper.

My body ached at the dinner table. It was the same simple food we had eaten the night before. After supper I watched the farmer and his wife play their game.

"Please do not make me dig again tomorrow. My back and arms have great pain. I must rest at least one day."

Old Man Chu said nothing.

His wife stood up and walked over to where I sat. "Take off your clothes," she said.

I worried at hearing the command but I did as she asked.

Maybe she was going to beat me?

The woman retrieved a jar from off the shelf. She opened it and scooped a handful of some kind of paste from the contents. It looked like honey.

I could smell it as she moved her hand from the jar. My eyes watered. It was not honey, not with a smell like that!

She pointed to the floor saying. "On your belly."

She began to rub the ointment all over my back and arms. She was not gentle. The pain was excruciating and comforting at the same time. I cried out in pain. The ointment burned like fire. I could feel it seeping into my skin, muscles, and bones.

When she quit, I felt like horses had run over my body. I was not sure I could get up and walk to my bedroll.

The old woman came back with a cup of what looked like a hot drink.

"Sit up and drink this," she said

It was steaming hot and smelled awful. I put the cup to my lips; it was bitter.

The old lady said, "The drink will relax your muscles. Drink it all. You will feel better in the morning."

I forced myself to drink. I wondered why the Master had sent me here? I felt tortured and there was no way I could or even wanted to find time to work on the puzzle.

I got up and made my way to my room. Suddenly euphoria swept through my body and soul. A feeling of peace and contentment enveloped me.

Just as my eyes closed I saw the puzzle in the corner. Disgust came over me. That was the last thing I remembered before drifting off.

Stress the Body/Clear the Mind

I woke to the sound of Old Man Chu's voice.

"Boy! Time to get up!"

It was as if I had just closed my eyes. I wanted to go back to sleep.

"My name is Shinhon, not boy."

The old man ignored me. "Breakfast in five minutes or you dig on an empty stomach."

My body still hurt but whatever was in the brew from the night before, and the tonic Tara rubbed on me, had made me feel better. I still dreaded digging the hole.

I dug, ate, slept, dug, ate, slept. At night, I looked at the puzzle before falling asleep thinking: There is no way I will ever be able to finish this assignment.

Every day was the same as the day before. I started to lose all the weight I had gained in the palace. As I lost the weight, the job became easier. I worked on the well for weeks, the days all blurring together.

Not only was my body getting stronger as I worked on the well, but my mind was more clear. In the Master's palace I had been filled with despair but now my mind was vibrant. I felt at peace.

Then one night as I watched Old Man Chu and Tara play their marble game I asked if I could bring out the puzzle.

"Yes," said Old Man Chu. "Why have you not done it sooner?"

I explained to him, "After being tortured every day digging that hole I did not want to look at the puzzle, but now my mind needs something to do."

Old Man Chu just looked at me. There was almost a smile on his face, at least as much of a smile as that crusty old man was capable of.

I worked for hours on the puzzle. I became obsessed with putting it together. My mind was racing and I was able to start connecting some pieces. I did get a border in place. Then Old Man Chu came to me and said that it was time to sleep.

The next day, while digging in the hole, I hit water. The water seeped into the well. It was pure and clean.

I climbed up the ladder and out of the hole, to find the old man.

The farm was well kept with everything in its place. As I looked for the old farmer, I noticed several mounds of dirt around the farm. I made a note to myself to ask Old Man Chu about them.

I found him in the pen with a few head of cattle. He had one hand in the bull's mouth and an arm around the massive animal's neck. I had no idea what he was doing but I did wonder how the old man could be that strong.

"I have finished the well," I yelled to him. He let the animal go and walked over to me.

I grinned at him and said, "I am finished! Now will you let me rest so I can concentrate on the real reason I am here... to put my puzzle together?"

The old man said with little emotion, "I thought the real reason you were here was to learn a wisdom of life," He didn't respond with a "thank you" or "good job" for finishing the well.

I said, "To learn the wisdom, I am to put the puzzle together, you ungrateful old man!"

He ignored me as usual and said, "Come with me."

Run Like the Wind

He put together a pack and two pouches of water. He gave me one pouch and said, "Let's go."

I asked, "Where are we going?"

The old man's finger rose up and pointed to the north where there were peaks of small mountains.

"There," he said.

I asked, "To those mountains? Why?"

"You ask too many questions." With that said, he took off running.

Surprised but determined, I ran to catch up. I am young and in better health than when I came to the farm. I had felt my body getting stronger each day. Now I would show this old man. I ran beside him for a minute then began to run faster and edged past him. It was fun running in the open air. This was much better than digging a hole.

"Come on old man," I taunted.

I ran a distance ahead of him, pulling further away. It got harder as I ran and my breathing became labored. I looked back at Old Man Chu. He was on my heels even though I was giving it all I had. The look on his face was surprising to me. He passed me, saying nothing. He showed no signs of exertion, as if he were taking a slow stroll.

Before long we were at the base of the mountain. It was steep. The old man did not miss a beat. Up he went while I struggled to catch my breath. He was unstoppable. How could this be? He must be super-human.

Was he going faster?

I watched as he ran farther and farther up the mountain, as he bounded over rocks and weeds with what looked like no effort.

I could no longer run, but only pull myself up step-by-step.

The old man looked to be close to the top, but when I got to that point, there were only more mountains. I could no longer see him.

At one point I knew my heart was going to jump out of my chest.

I made it to the top of the mountain. There sat the old man on a boulder, surveying the valley, looking down on his farm. It was beautiful. As I stood at the top, I passed out and blackness encircled me. I awoke beside the boulder. My face was wet. The old man must have splashed water on me. I was surprised he did not leave me there to die.

"Your body is weak," Old Man Chu said without much feeling in his voice.

I replied, "And your manners are bad, so what? Did you bring me up here to kill me?

He had a real smile on his face as he said, "I have climbed this same rock every day for fifty years. The rest of your stay you will run it with me."

Stress on the Body Stimulates the Mind

"I do not understand this. I am learning nothing only how much abuse I can take."

Old Man Chu looked out over the vastness and said "It is beautiful. Did you see the fox as we came up the hill? Or the deer? This place is sacred."

I looked at him and said, "I saw nothing! I was just trying to stay alive."

The old man began to lecture me, "Yes, in the world people are always just trying to stay alive and usually with the least amount of effort, but effort is what keeps us alive. Striving for more makes life fulfilled. Shinhon, those who look for rest and shortcuts in life are often left behind, and many times become lost and forgotten. What pushes you makes you not only stronger but wiser. You do not want to know what is easier but what is more efficient. My body is efficient and yours is not. With a strong body comes a more effective mind. Your mind is not yet awake."

We sat and looked out over the valley. I pondered over what he had said.

That night my mind was on fire with intense thoughts, and as I worked on the puzzle, the pieces snapped into place. I was astounded by how effortless it was.

The next day Old Man Chu woke me up even earlier and off we went up the steepest part of the mountain. When at the top, we talked. Like a magical place, this sacred mountaintop opened the old man's mouth. He would talk to me of the body and mind, and the connection between them.

"Why do we run up this mountain every day?" Old Man Chu asked me.

"Because you are a crazy old man," I replied.

"No… it is because the stress on the body stimulates the mind. If the body does not run well, neither will the mind. Did you not feel your mind racing as your blood pumped when reaching the top of the mountain?"

"Yes, I do feel much more alive on the mountaintop. I feel good." I took in a deep breath of the cool intoxicating air.

"You feel alive because of what it took to get here," he said.

With that, he jumped off his rock and sprinted down the treacherous mountain.

The farm work was hard. We moved hay and pillars of wood for fences. I could just barely keep up with the old man.

The days went by and my body became rock solid. I could now out-run the old man. I waited for him at the top of the mountain, enjoying the few minutes I had to myself. I worked on the puzzle every night and each new piece fit together easily. I knew it would be finished soon.

A Person Can Be More Than One Thing

I grew to love Old Man Chu and his wife Tara. He did not say much but I could feel softness in his heart. Tara was quiet in a happy sort of way. She hummed to herself as she went throughout her day. They were simple people, living a good, simple, happy life.

The nightmares of my family stopped. I was able to concentrate on the love I had for them instead of all the pain I felt. I was glad for the good memories.

My mind and body were sharper than ever; more and more I felt like I was at one with the First Wisdom.

The last piece of the puzzle was now in place. It was a beautiful work of art.

The artisan that made it must have been an amazing engineer.

Old Man Chu stood before me looking at the puzzle. "So you have finally finished my puzzle."

I looked at him in wonder, "Your puzzle? What do you mean?"

"I created it and gave it to the Master," he said. "I crafted it out of a single piece of wood."

"I thought you were only a farmer," I said to him.

The Old Man grinned at me saying, "A person can be more than one thing."

Old Man Chu took the puzzle and placed it on the fireplace.

"It looks good here again," he said.

"When you feel you are ready and have learned what you have come here to learn you may go to the Master and tell him the puzzle is finished and back where it belongs."

I did not want to leave so I stayed for several more weeks. I ran up the mountain and worked the farm every day. There was always something to do. I was happy there.

Thank You

One day, as I was walking with Old Man Chu, I looked at the mounds of dirt that were scattered around the farm.

"Old Man Chu," I asked, "What are all those mounds of dirt? Do they serve a purpose for the farm?"

"They are old wells," he said.

"What do you mean old wells?" I asked.

"You are not the only one the Master has sent to me. I will fill the old well after you leave."

The next morning Old Man Chu did not find me in bed when he came to get me for our run. He found me at the old well.

"What are you doing boy?" he asked.

As I shoveled more dirt into the hole, I said, "I am filling in the old well so you do not have to."

The old man looked puzzled.

I told Old Man Chu, "Because I am grateful for you and for all I have learned from you and Tara."

Surpise and pleasure flooded his face.

It took me many days to fill the well. After I was finished, I knew that the First Wisdom was part of me. I was ready to leave the farm.

Old Man Chu and Tara were like family but I knew I must leave.

That night I told them that it was time for me to return to the Master.

Old Man Chu put his hand on my shoulder. "No one else has ever filled the well. Thank you, Shinhon."

I had been on the farm for months but never heard Old Man Chu say thank you for anything. I knew there was a strong lesson to learn and something inside me said I would comprehend it someday.

The Physical

I was ready the next day. Tara made food for my travel to the palace. She kissed me on the check with a tear in her eye.

Old Man Chu said, "Goodbye, Master Shinhon. You have a good heart and a strong spirit."

Then he turned towards the barn and was gone. I walked the same path that I traveled to come here, turning back once to wave at Tara.

I decided I would run all the way to the palace. I ran over hills, mountains and streams. My body was perfect. My mind pondered all I had learned as I ran, and most of all I enjoyed the beauty of this land.

I ran through the night, letting my mind guide me, never feeling tired.

The guards were in their place, just as they were the first time I saw them.

"Tell the Master that Shinhon, his apprentice, has returned," I announced.

It was not long before the guard returned and motioned for me to follow. He guided me into the great room, and as before, the Master sat on the beautiful chair.

The Master looked me over with approval, as my body was now like a sculpted statue.

"I see the puzzle is not with you." His blue eyes glowed.

I said "Old Man Chu told me to let you know that the puzzle is now back where it belongs."

"Very good," the Master said and then added, "Have you learned the First Wisdom?"

I thought for a moment.

"Yes, I have, Master," I said.

The Master beckoned. "Tell me all you have learned."

"I have never worked as hard as I did on Old Man Chu's farm. Muscles I did not know existed reminded me they did, indeed, exist. After a while, I noticed my body no longer ached and I felt strong. Old Man Chu put me through stress but he worked as an equal beside me."

"Old Man Chu," the Master laughed at the name I had given the farmer.

"I am one with the First Wisdom, Master. The First Wisdom is of the physical. The wisdom connects with our body and mind. As we test our bodies, our minds sharpen and as we eat food close to the earth, our bodies operate more efficiently and our mind becomes clear."

The Master watched me, stroking his beard.

"In the palace as I sat and ate and looked at the puzzle, my mind was cloudy. I felt lost and miserable. I could not concentrate on the puzzle. As my body grew from the hard work at the farm, everything changed. My mind improved and the puzzle became easy to put together. My mind focused. Master, I see the importance of this wisdom."

"Shinhon, as you stay strong, you will take on all facets in your life, whether physical, mental or spiritual. The First Wisdom is important for life and is the most basic of all the Eight Wisdoms. Stress your body and feed it good fuel. It will never hinder your growth."

WISDOM

2

"Take the attitude of a student, never be too big to ask questions, never know too much to learn something new."

OG MANDINO

The Merchant

The master looked at me and pondered for a moment. He spoke slowly as he said, "The second Wisdom is important to connect with the others. Are you ready?"

I looked at him with determination and replied, "Yes, Master."

"You are to go to the city of Hiin, the biggest city of my lands. You are to search out the merchant, Chinsha. You are to be his servant and learn. After you learn all you can from him you will be directed to General Yosha. After assisting General Yosha, you will come back to me. Travel to the city is only half a day. You will be given provisions. You can leave for the city in the morning."

"Yes Master. A night's sleep would do me well."

The next day I left for the city of Hiin to the north of the Master's palace, with nothing but the clothes on my back and a note to Chinsha from the Master.

I ran to the great city. It was a massive metropolis. A boy like me had never seen such a place. I had never seen so many people.

I could not imagine so many buildings. I was dizzy with the hustle and bustle of the city. I asked a man inside the entrance where the merchant Chinsha lived. He explained that the great businessman lived in the northeast part of the city. As I walked in that direction I watched in awe. Merchants on the street were selling items I had only heard of, and some I did not know existed. There was a big market with vendors hawking their wares, buying and selling. Eventually I reached the door of the merchant's home.

I expected a great palace, but as beautiful as Chinsha's home was and bigger than any house I had ever seen, it was nothing like the Master's fortress. I knocked on the door. A large man answered scowling down at me.

I asked if he was the merchant, Chinsha. "No," said the man, "I am his servant. What do you want?"

I explained to him that The Master told me to go to the merchant's home. "Chinsha sees no one without an appointment," barked the servant.

"I have an appointment with Chinsha," I replied.

I reached in my pocket and took out the small scroll. "Here, I have a letter from the Master." The servant took the note and told me to wait outside.

A few minutes later the servant opened the door and asked me to come in.

The merchant's home was magnificent. I was not familiar with great wealth but even I could see that the items in the home were valuable.

I was led to a great room where an older man sat smoking a pipe by a fireplace, stoked with a nice warm fire. I stood in the middle of the room. I wasn't sure if I should interrupt his meditation. Without looking around he spoke. "So the Master has sent you to me. Do you know why you are here?"

I assumed the man was Chinsha. I explained that the Master did not give me explicit reasons, only that I was to learn the Second Wisdom of life and to work for you as your servant until I finish the tasks you set before me.

With a wise look on his face Chinsha turned to me and said, "Please dine with my daughter and me. Enjoy the evening with us. Your work begins tomorrow."

The house was elegant and I looked forward to learning the wisdom in such a pleasing environment.

I was led to a dining room with a large table. The merchant pointed to a young girl waiting for us. He introduced her as his daughter Aryia. "Hello," she said. She was a beautiful little girl with a sweet smile.

I tipped my head toward her and said, "Hello, Chinsha's daughter."

The meal was pleasant with excellent food. I did not eat too much as I was now part of the physical wisdom and my body craved good foods in a sparing manner. The merchant was pleasant and his daughter was charming. The merchant told me he had lost his wife during childbirth. He looked over at his daughter and said Aryia was his greatest gift, above any earthly treasure.

After the extravagant meal I went to my room. The merchant reminded me that the next day would be busy so I should get as much rest as possible.

What Do You Want?

I was awakened before sunrise and given some clothing to wear. After breakfast I was told to go to the main stables of the city and there I would receive further instructions.

The main stables of the great city had many animals. The stench was awful.

I walked up to a foul man who looked as if he was in charge. He looked at me and said with a slurred voice, "Are you here to work?" Yes," I said. After a few simple instructions I started working. Old Man Chu's farm stables were nothing like this.

I was given a pitchfork and told to go to the far west stalls and scour them out. This was the filthiest area of the stables. A little hay mixed with feces and urine, but mostly the latter. The ammonia smell made it hard to breath.

What am I supposed to learn from this? How can this teach me about the Second Wisdom?

The stableman brought me a piece of bread with a little goat's cheese, after hours of working and sweating. I thought of Old Man Chu. Unlike this man, Chu had always cared about me. He had an unspoken love in his heart.

My muscles enjoyed the work but my sense of smell did not.

The hours passed and soon the man returned to the stables and told me that I was finished for the day.

How could I go to the merchant's home looking and smelling like this? I was so filthy.

A servant met me at the front of the house. I was told to go to the side room where there was a washing area. I took off the nasty clothing and cleaned myself as best I could. New clothes were set out for me.

Once again I was led to the dining room where the merchant and his daughter sat chatting with each other. Aryia was telling her father about her day. The merchant listened to every word she said. He nodded his head once in a while and smiled at her enthusiasm. Her face radiated kindness as she smiled.

She noticed me standing there. "So good to see you, Shinhon," she said. "How was your first day in the city?"

I explained to her that I worked hard on the farms of Old Man Chu but I have never worked in such filth as I did today. It was an unpleasant experience.

"The main stables of the town can get quite messy," said the merchant.

More like an explosion of waste and noxious ammonia. Messy isn't the right word!

The rest of the dinner was pleasant with small talk as the merchant asked me questions. I told parts of my life in the village and also how I came to be the Master's apprentice.

The next day, I put on more ragged clothes and headed for the stables. Yesterday I had cleaned out every stall so I thought it might be easier today. But no! It was more of the same. Each stall looked as though it had never been cleaned.

The foul man left as he did the day before, only coming back to give me a hard piece of bread, dried up cheese, and a canteen of water.

A week passed and the work never improved or got easier. My body enjoyed the work but I did not. The merchant told me at dinner that night that I would no longer need to clean the stables. That was the best news.

I was awakened in the morning and given new clothing that looked like the rags I wore to clean the stables. I told the servant that the merchant said I would not clean the stables today. He smiled at me and said, "Yes, you have a new task today."

I was led to a different area where a man was awaiting my arrival. He explained that I was to work on the viaducts that take human waste out of the city. This inter-connected system flowed behind the buildings and houses. He explained that although it was a engineering masterpiece, the connections needed to be cleaned often or the sewage would back up.

I was given instructions on what to do to keep the sewers from clogging and the methods for cleaning them out.

How could this possibly teach me anything about anything?

Nausea consumed me and my morning breakfast left my body. I wished I were back at the stables cleaning animal waste. I learned that animal waste was not nearly as repulsive as human waste.

I went home that night ready to tell the merchant I could no longer do that horrible job. When I arrived I was led to the side door where I was to wash. I tried to relax and enjoy the water, scrubbing human feces out of my hair, but I was angry. I was told to eat with the servants. The fact that I was not invited to dine with Aryia and the merchant did not improve my mood. After more than a week on this revolting job, my mood was as foul as the viaducts. Finally, I was asked to dine again with the merchant.

All cleaned with nice clothing on my back, I walked into the dining room. There sat Chinsha and his sweet daughter, a smile on her face as she saw me walk to the table.

"Hello, Shinhon." Aryia said as I sat down.

"Hello, Aryia." I looked at Chinsha and nodded with less than my usual enthusiasm.

"How is your work going in the city?" asked Chinsha.

Not so good I told him, trying my best not to show the anger I felt. I have learned nothing of any life wisdom in the depths of the city's waste.

"Oh really," said the merchant. "Do you not like the work?"

"No, Chinsha. I do not like it in the least. Actually, I hate it."

"Why don't you quit?" Aryia asked with sweet innocence.

I turned my head to her saying, "I am here to learn the wisdoms of life and I gave my word to the Master to complete whatever is asked of me."

"You must have learned something with the two tasks presented to you," said the merchant.

Frustrated I looked at him saying, "Yes, I have learned that this is not what I want to do."

"That is an important lesson," said the merchant. "Knowing what you don't want makes it a lot easier to find what you do want." "You may achieve anything in life if you want to, but you may not put forth the effort because you do not pursue what you love. People settle for anything because they do not know their own self-worth. Knowing what you don't want out of life is one step away from being what you were put on this earth to be. To find out who you are, you must know who you are not."

As I was mulling over what the merchant said, he surprised me by speaking again. "What would you like from me? What can I teach you?"

I thought about that question for a minute. "I would like to learn how to become rich like you."

The merchant smiled, "The man who administers the sewers is a very wealthy man. He is one of the richest men in this city. No one will do what he does so the city pays him handsomely to do the job that no one else will do."

With a grimace on my face I said, "I can see why but I do not want to be wealthy that way. I would like to vend like you, buying and selling merchandise."

"So be it," said the merchant. "You will come to me in the morning and begin your new task as a merchant."

Fail to Learn

The next day The merchant asked me if I was ready for my next task? I told him I was excited to get started. He explained to me that I would go into the city again, but this time I would learn to sell merchandise. The merchant pulled a beautiful necklace out of a blue velvet box.

Chinsha said, "This is a valuable necklace. You are to go far west of the city to the wealthy merchant Chicon. There, you are to sell this necklace to him for 200 gold pieces."

Two hundred gold pieces is more money than I had ever seen. Chinsha handed the necklace to me and told me to go. I shoved the necklace into my pocket on the inside of my ragged jacket.

It took me some time to find Chicon's home. I admired the massive, elaborate mansion which looked more like I thought Chinsha's home would look. Large pillars held up the front porch with exquisite designs twisted around each one, along with ornate sculptured foliage. The massive double doors were at least twenty feet tall. I could feel my confidence ebbing.

I walked up to the imposing doors and knocked. It was some time before anyone answered. Finally an old man with white hair and a stringy white beard appeared.

"What do you want?" he asked.

"My name is Shinhon." He shifted from one foot to the other, looking impatient for me to tell him what I wanted.

"Go on, spit it out boy, what do you want?"

"I have brought this very valuable necklace from Chinsha the merchant, for Chicon. I was directed to tell Chicon that he could buy it for only 200 gold pieces."

The servant looked infuriated. "Get out of here you filthy peasant. Master Chicon doesn't want stolen merchandize. Get out of here or I will call the guards." He pushed me backward and I stumbled.

I was in shock but explained to him that I got the necklace from the merchant, Chinsha. I did not steal it. I traveled here to sell it to Chicon.

"Get out of here," the old man said again and pointed his crooked finger in my face. "If I ever see you again I will make sure you are severely punished. I will have your hands cut off for stealing that worthless piece of metal you call a necklace. You will rot in jail for a very long time." With that, the old man slammed the door.

What could I do? I could not go back to the merchant with my task undone. I decided I would stand behind the massive pillar and wait for Chicon. I knew if I could only talk to him I could sell him this piece of jewelry.

I waited a long time and saw many people come and go. They all looked important and distinguished. I thought of my shabby appearance and understood why the man would not talk to me. Not with all the magnificent people that came to the door. Some were sent away as I was.

Then several people outside the great doors grew excited. In the middle of the crowd a man was being treated with great respect. I reasoned that this man must be Chicon.

As he came closer I stepped up, "Hello, Chicon." I was feeling brave, bold, and was determined to succeed.

I held up the necklace for him to see. "Chinsha, the merchant, sent me to sell you this beautiful necklace."

Guards swarmed around me. The angry looks on their faces made me think they wouldn't hesitate to attack me.

"How dare you speak to the great Chicon?" one of the guards said.

Chicon did not even look at the necklace or me. He said to one of the men, "Give him a copper coin and send him on his way."

I was thrown some copper pieces and admonished that if I ever came to this house or tried to converse with Chicon again, there would be serious consequences. I left in a hurry, fearing what they might do. I could not even talk to Chicon so there is no way that I could sell him this necklace. I had failed at such a simple task. The man could afford ten necklaces like the one I held. He was decorated with multiple pieces of jewelry. I knew if he looked at my necklace he would want it but he would not even look at it. What could I do but walk back to the home of Chinsha?

A servant met me at the side entrance, "Just in time for dinner; Chinsha is waiting for you." He said.

Food was repulsive to me and I did not want to see the merchant, but I followed.

The merchant and his daughter were chatting at the dining table. "Come in boy, did you sell the necklace?" asked the merchant.

I lowered my head in despair and said, "No, sir. I have failed at this task. I am a failure at selling and have learned nothing. Only that selling is not as easy as I thought. Chicon would not even see me. Some accused me of stealing the necklace and even called the necklace a piece of junk. One threatened to remove my hands and throw me in jail."

The merchant laughed. "Failure is often the perfect teacher. Something that is too easy is sometimes easily forgotten. But, something that is difficult can stick in our minds forever. Failure is one of the most important lessons in life. It proves your desire for what you want. If you fail and give up, then you know it was not your true desire. When you succeed after failure, then you have learned something in a way that will assist you in always remembering the lesson. If it was not a challenge, then the lesson is forgotten. I want you to go back to Chicon's home tomorrow and sell the necklace."

Risk

I pondered what the merchant had said and was concerned for my own safety. I explained to him that I couldn't go back because I was warned that if I were to go back again, I would be put in jail or see my hands cut off or both. I like my hands and want to keep them.

"A great teacher in life is risk," said the merchant.

I said in a worried voice, "Risk? Once again I thought of risking my hands and my freedom.

He further explained that fear keeps many from taking risks, but those who take risks learn more than those who become complacent. Without adversity you will never know how great you can be. Those who grow comfortable in their life never do more than live life. Those that have courage to face can change the world.

I thought about all the risks I had taken to get where I was today. A warm feeling came over me and my confidence grew.

He looked at me with eyes that penetrated my thoughts.

"Shinhon… a foolish man runs blindly into a risky situation. But a smart man thinks through the risks and focuses on what to do to create a positive outcome."

I replied. "I see that a life without hands, spent in jail, is not a good outcome for anyone,"

"You are right, young man," said Chinsha. "What could you do to minimize the risk and avert a bad outcome?"

I shrugged my shoulders and told him I had no idea.

"If you did know… then what would that look like?" Chinsha asked.

I thought about the day I visited Chicon's house and about all the people who were permitted to enter. I noticed what set these people apart from me. They were well dressed.

I told Chinsha that the people who were permitted to enter the house were always dressed in fine clothing. If I dressed extravagantly I would not be remembered as the ragged boy from the day before.

"Excellent, I will have my servants dress you in fine clothing and expensive jewelry," Chinsha said.

I thought for a moment and said, "There is still a risk that Chicon will not see me, but you are well respected. Maybe you could write a letter presenting me as a trusted salesman. I would look presentable and have your letter to prove I am a man worthy of respect. I could also present the necklace in a different manner than just holding it up in my hand. Maybe I should display the necklace on velvet and make it as presentable as myself."

I thought about placing the necklace in a beautiful case, instead of just taking it out of my pocket like a common thief. I would have believed the worst also if I had seen a raggedy boy taking something as fine as that necklace out of his pocket.

"I do have many ornate cases in my collection," the merchant said. "Go pick out whatever you want."

The jewelry box I picked out was inlaid with beautiful purple velvet and the box was well crafted. It included a lock and key. I was confident that this would make the necklace look even more elegant and valuable. I put it in my jacket.

The merchant wrote a letter of recommendation and stamped it with his seal. He told me to get a good night's sleep. I slept well and soon it was morning. I left for Chicon's house once again, prepared to sell the necklace.

As I got closer to Chicon's house I began to worry about the servant. Would he recognize me? What if I was put in jail? I was getting a little nervous. Then I thought about what the merchant had said, that risk was how good men became great. I knew that I must be confident at the door.

I rapped on the door with the large lion's head knocker.

The same old servant opened it.

"What is your business, young man?" asked the servant, looking at me much differently this time. "How may I help you?"

He did not recognize me.

"I come from the home of the great merchant Chinsha. I am one of his salesmen. Here is my letter of recommendation from Master Chinsha. I have a great treasure that I am sure will interest Chicon."

The servant looked me up and down. "Do I know you boy?"

I felt the sweat bead on my forehead.

"No, I do not believe so, sir," I said softly.

"What is it?" the servant asked looking interested.

I put my hand on the pocket containing the treasure and explained to him that I was directed to show the prize to no one but Chicon. He told me he would give the letter to his master. The servant left me standing outside once again, but this time he came back.

He announced that Master Chicon would see me and invited me in as he was eager to see the treasure. I was led through a great hall into a big chamber adorned with exotic art and treasures. The wealthy man was reclining on a floor of pillows. He held the letter from Chinsha in his hand.

Chicon smiled at me and remarked, "Such respect from the old merchant for someone so young. It says you are one of Chinsha's trusted salesmen. I wish to see this great treasure."

I took the key from my pocket and turned the lock on the box carefully, in anticipation of showing him the treasure. The necklace did look beautiful the way it was presented. Even I felt that it was a great treasure. I could see in the man's eyes that he too found it magnificent.

"How much is Chinsha asking for the necklace?" Chicon responded.

I thought about the price that Chinsha told me. He had said 200 gold pieces but I hesitated. "Master, this is a valuable piece and very rare. You will never find its equal anywhere."

He asked impatiently, "Yes, yes, how much does Chinsha want?" He did not wait for an answer. "I will give 400 gold pieces and not a copper more!"

That is double what Chinsha asked! I thought, amazed.

Trying hard to hide my excitement, I accepted the offer on behalf of Chinsha and congratulated Chicon on owning such a treasure.

Win/Win

I went back to the merchant excited and happy feeling accomplished and alive. Now I understood what Chinsha meant about failure, success, and risk.

I traveled back to the merchant's home and found him sitting in his study. He looked up at me and asked if I had sold the necklace.

"Yes I did, Chinsha," I said with excitement in my voice.

He inquired, "How much did you get for it?"

"I got 400 gold pieces," I said, grinning from ear to ear.

"Excellent," said Chinsha. "I asked 200 gold for the necklace and you have made a profit for yourself of 200 gold. How does it feel to be a wealthy man?"

I did not expect that. I thought all the money was Chinsha's.

Seeing the look on my face, Chinsha said "I only asked for 200 gold pieces but you allowed Chacon to purchase it for what he felt it was worth. You have earned the extra gold. I bought the necklace for 100 gold pieces, but in cities to the east it could easily sell for a 1000 gold pieces. We have all made an honest profit. In life, if you look for situations or opportunities in which all concerned will benefit in some way, you will be sought out for your fairness and good dealings. This one aspect in business can create riches. Doing good to others begets others doing good to you. This in turn will attract more opportunities for you to succeed."

"As you look for opportunities to assist those around you, you will be blessed. Always look for the win/win in life and you will make more of a difference in the world. Go to bed now. I will have something else for you to sell tomorrow."

I went to bed thinking of the many things I had learned that day. I was excited and eager to learn more.

Keep Going

The next day I woke up ready and eager to take on the next challenge. In my mind I had learned the secrets to selling. Now I could be a wealthy man. I was excited to see the next item Chinsha wanted me to sell. It would be easy. I smiled to myself and thought about all the things that I could tell the Master that I had learned.

That morning I dressed in fine clothing. No more rags for me. I met with Chinsha and Aryia for the morning meal. We talked back and forth. I told the merchant how grateful I was for learning so much.

I asked Chinsha what he would like for me to sell next? Another piece of expensive jewelry or some very fine clothing, or maybe a great home.

With a smile Chinsha said, "Here, it is beside me," I looked beside him and all I saw was what looked like a bucket filled with dirt.

I asked ironically, "Is that a bucket filled with dirt?"

Yes, the dirt is from the Helain Mountains to the northeast. It is valuable dirt with special properties. I want 100 gold pieces for the bucket," Chinsha explained.

Astonished I asked "What? one hundred gold pieces for a bucket of dirt? That is crazy! There is no way I can get that price."

The merchant laughed. "I told you it is special dirt and is very valuable."

Dirt is dirt.

I was well dressed, but I could not find an elegant bucket so I left the dirt in the same bucket. Confused, I took the item and left that morning.

Chinsha had assured me that this was special dirt from the Helain mountains and I didn't question his knowledge. Still, I had to wonder why anyone would pay that much for a bucket of dirt.

That first day everyone just laughed when I asked if they wanted to buy a bucket of dirt. No one was interested at all.

I went back to Chinsha at the end of the day. "Is this a joke," I asked him? "Everyone thinks I'm crazy because I am trying to sell dirt, especially for that price."

Chinsha corrected me saying, "Helain mountain dirt." He assured me it was not a joke.

Day after day I left Chinsha's house with the dirt and everyday people would laugh at me. I traveled throughout the city becoming familiar with all its aspects. People began talking about the crazy boy who was trying to sell dirt. One week turned into two and two turned into three. I begged Chinsha to give me something else to sell but he refused. I told him that I was not the salesman I thought I had become.

He explained to me that succeeding is just about being persistent until the right person comes along at the right time.

I enjoyed talking at meals with Chinsha and Aryia. I asked Chinsha if there was anything more I could do, because selling dirt was not going so well. He said to concentrate on the task at hand and sell the dirt. Then he would give me a new task.

I was getting discouraged and felt there was no way I was going to sell the dirt. I enjoyed the city as I watched the merchants in the market place. I learned how they made deals and bartered with one another, as well as many other things about business. I saw how a merchant bought cloth from an other vendor and then the next day made the cloth into a covering, selling it for twice as much as it originally cost. I found that business was interesting to me. I began to understand that an item only sold if it was wanted. My dirt was not wanted.

Distraught, I noticed a man in the market frantically talking to people. One of the merchants pointed at me. The man ran toward me as fast as he could. He had a determined look in his eyes. He stood in front of me and asked, excitedly, "Are you the boy with the Helain Mountain dirt?"

"Yes." I said, "It is in this bucket I have in my hand."

"Is it from the eastern top of the mountain, the part that is said to have healing powers?" he asked.

I said, "I was told that it is special dirt and you can only get it from the Helain Mountains."

"I will give you ten pieces of gold for it," the man said.

"Ten pieces of gold. That is not enough," I told him.

The man said in a pleading voice, "It is all the money I possess. I would give you more if I had it. I have been traveling everywhere looking for this special dirt as I was told that it was the only thing that would cure my sick wife. She is ill and close to death. This dirt mixed with water makes a mud that has special healing powers and can take the sickness from my wife. I will do anything to save her life.

"I come from the small port city of Bahe in the southeast. I would go to the mountains myself but the journey would take too long and my beloved wife would die before I got back. When I heard of someone selling this precious dirt, I knew that my prayers to the Great Spirit had been answered."

"I don't believe in a Great Spirit but I am glad you found me," I replied with compassion.

I thought of the man and the love he had for his wife as well as his willingness to give his entire life savings for this dirt. I was filled with empathy as thoughts of my own family flashed through my mind. I would have done anything to save them.

I told the man that the merchant I sell for wanted 100 gold pieces for this dirt.

His face turned to anguish. "All hope is lost," he said with a sigh of despair.

I felt compassion for him as I looked at the sadness in his eyes. I told the man that I would take 10 gold pieces.

He began to cry. "I will be forever indebted to you. What is your name?" he asked.

I replied, "Shinhon."

His voice quivered as he said, "I will never forget you Master Shinhon. I know you will become a great man and leader someday."

On a piece of parchment he wrote his name as Colayin and the name of the city he lived in as Bahe. He said if I was ever in Bahe to find him so he could repay me for my kindness.

We exchanged the dirt for the 10 gold pieces. Then he hurried on his way.

I had sold the dirt, which seemed worthless to me, but there was a warm feeling in my heart. I still had 200 gold pieces from my sale of the necklace. I would give Chinsha 90 gold pieces and still be richer then I could have imagined.

I was excited and rushed to tell the merchant.

I got to the merchant's home by mid-day. Chinsha was not there but I talked with Aryia. She was so smart for such a young girl. I reminisced on how her life must have been as her father raised her. She was happy to know that I had sold the dirt. I told her the story.

"You are a good person with a good heart." she said as she smiled.

How sweet she was, I thought as I said, "It is you, little girl, who has the good heart."

When Chinsha came home, I repeated my story and gave him the 100 pieces of gold for the dirt—10 pieces I had received and 90 of my own.

He was pleased and explained to me that the universe remembers your deeds in life. Karma is a strong power and the way you treat others will always come back to you. The Great Spirit will bless you. Cause and effect is paramount in this life.

I told him, "I don't believe in all those things, but I do know that my heart guided me and I felt only compassion for the man and his wife. My only hope is that his wife will live."

Chinsha said that the dirt made a powerful healing mud and that he was certain she would be saved.

Do More
Learn More

Chinsha and I sat and talked for some time. He said, "I have another task for you. This does not require selling. The great clock tower in the middle of the city is no longer working and needs repair. No one has been able to fix it. You are a bright young man and I have faith that you can repair the clock."

"I don't know anything about clocks," was my reply.

"The best way to learn is by doing," said Chinsha. "When the clock is repaired you will be given 200 gold pieces."

Two hundred gold pieces! Chinsha throws giant sums of money around as if it were nothing. How could I comprehend such wealth and prosperity.

"You will start tomorrow," he stated.

I began the task and after six months of going to the clock tower I felt that I was no closer to fixing the clock than when I started. There were so many mechanisms and gears.

After dismantling the clock I was able to learn how many peices worked together. Sometimes I went to bed with my mind aching, thinking about the genuis of these interconnections. Chinsha would ask me every day how I was progressing with the clock and if I was any closer to getting it repaired. The answer was always the same.

"No!"

I loved being with Chinsha as I was treated like family. They were all kind to me. Seven months had passed when I stood before Chinsha. "This was a trick," I shouted. "There was nothing wrong with the clock. After seven months I have found that one small screw was not secure. This tiny screw out of the thousands of parts of the clock was the sole problem that kept it from working. What a useless waste of time."

Chinsha stopped me saying, "You are angry."

"Yes!" I said. "Because this was such a waste."

"Why was it a waste?" he said? "You did fix the clock didn't you?"

"Yes, but it took so long for something so simple," I mumbled.

"You just earned 200 gold pieces? That is more than you or most others have ever seen in a lifetime."

I felt ashamed as I realized there was a lesson in what I had learned with the clock: As I did more I learned more.

"Yes, Chinsha," I said feeling humble.

Chinsha said, "Tell me what you learned about the clock."

"I know everything about the clock's workings. I know where each piece goes and in what place."

"So you could say that you are a master clocksmith. Could you build one if you had the parts?"

"Yes, I could build one." I said.

The merchant asked, "If you were offered 200 gold pieces again to fix this problem, how long would it take you."

"Maybe a minute," I replied.

Only then did I realize fully what I had learned.

Chinsha explained to me that over the last seven months I had received a valuable education and could now make 200 gold pieces in one minute, certainly not a waste of time.

I whispered. "I now understand."

"You have learned much young man. Aryia and I have enjoyed your company."

"I have enjoyed both you and Aryia as well. I will regret leaving this place."

Chinsha put his hand on my shoulder and said, "I've taught you all the lessons you can learn from me. It is time for you to go. There is a caravan leaving tomorrow. It will be going to the north to replenish supplies for the army of General Yosha. The general is waiting for you. The Master has asked that you see the general at once. Don't forget us, Shinhon, and come back to visit. I would love to hear of your future adventures."

I knew it was time to leave, but this seemed too sudden. I hugged him. I had grown to love and respect Chinsha and Aryia. He explained that Aryia would be sad to see me go. I told him I would miss her as well and I loved her as though she were my little sister.

The next day I was ready for the caravan to go to the war front. Aryia was sad indeed. She cried, making me feel awkward. She gave me a necklace. On it was a beautiful bronzed hand with four fingers outstretched and the thumb held to the palm, representing the number four.

With tears in her eyes she said, "This is a symbol of friendship. Please remember me, Shinhon. Please come back and see us someday." She cried as she ran away, not wanting to see me leave.

Chinsha embraced me, "Be safe and take care. You are going to a dangerous place."

I left his beautiful home, riding in an uncomfortable caravan, excited about the future but sad to leave my friends. I closed my eyes, satisfied that I had completed the mission and humbled by the powerful lessons I had learned from the master merchant, Chinsha. I knew this was just the beginning.

The General

The caravan smelled of sheep, camels, and dirty caravan drivers. The aroma of rotten food made me queasy. I didn't ask what it was and only ate enough to stay alive. This made me miss the comfort of Chinsha's home. I continued stressing my body by running with the caravan and felt good at night sleeping under the open sky.

When the caravan stopped for the day, the crew sat around the campfire drinking, eating greasy food, and throwing unwanted pieces to the animals. It was not comfortable but no worse than the viaducts of the city of Hiin.

After a long journey, our caravan entered the outposts of the army city. There were hundreds of tents lined up; dull beige-gray goat hides were the soldiers' homes. This base was bigger than most cities, covering many miles. The caravan was met by soldiers, fast at work.

One soldier talked to the leader of the caravan, who turned and pointed to me. The soldier explained that the general was expecting me and asked me to follow him. This was a soldier who had seen many battles. His long, brown hair flowed down the sides of his shoulders. Through the hardness in the man's eyes, his face shined with a special goodness.

He led me to the middle of the tent city. There stood a large tent, much bigger than the others. I assumed this must be General Yosha's.

The man knocked on the board positioned at the side of the tent door. After a few minutes, a large warrior appeared looking like he was made of steel. He wore hard leather clothing, no more ornate than the solders I had seen so far, but I knew that this man was not just a regular soldier. His long hair was pulled back into a pony tail, his beard trimmed tight. There was gray on top of his head and on both sides of his face. Standing next to him, without a word spoken, I felt the respect his presence demanded. He looked down at me.

The soldier guiding me said, "This is the one you were expecting."

"I am General Yosha." His voice sounded like a deep growl.

He looked at the solder beside me, "this is Makato, a valued officer in my army. He has been instructed to assist and direct you in your time with us."

Looking into Makato's brown eyes I saw the spirit of a warrior and a holy man.

The general looked at Makato, "Go get the boy washed up and fed. I will send for him tomorrow."

Makato shook his head and bid me follow him.

As we left for our destination, he talked. It was amazing to listen to such a soft kind voice coming from someone who appeared so hardened by life.

"So, you are the one we were told to expect from the latest caravan."

I responded, "Yes, I guess I am."

"Good, good, we have anticipated your arrival for days. Glad to see you are safe and sound from your journey." He held out a huge hand. I reached for it and we shook. He smiled at me with a pleasant expression that lit up his face.

"Let's get you washed and fed. This is when we gather around the campfire, eat and talk—it is a time that soldiers can discuss the day's events. I will get the necessary supplies that you will need to keep in your pack. The soldiers are instructed to respect others, so items are seldom stolen, but we do move a lot, sometimes quickly, and things can get lost."

I asked him what the punishment was if someone was caught stealing. He commented that it is at the discretion of the commanding officer but the punishment could be severe and he also stated again with a smile that they did not have a problem with stealing. He explained that I should just take care of my own pack and I would have no problems.

Makato took me to the place where the men cleaned themselves. It was a small river by the camp. I washed my body; the water felt good. By the time I finished Makato had left and returned with a soldier's uniform and a new pack. "Here you are, my young soldier," he said in a comforting voice.

Was I a soldier?

I dressed in the hard and heavy clothing. Makato lead me to the officers' campfire. They gathered around one by one. The sun was setting and the scorched tent city cooled.

What Is a Leader?

Makato signaled me to sit at the campfire. He handed me a container filled with all the eating utensils I would need. We all took turns filling our plates with food.

The men were curious about me and asked what a young boy was doing here. I said, "I do not know, the Master sent me."

I asked a few of the men to tell me about the general. General Yosha became the main topic of conversation the rest of the night. The entire group of soldiers spoke highly of him. After listening for a while, I began asking questions as to why they believed Yosha was such a great leader.

Everyone around the campfire had input, each spoke of insight as to why General Yosha was a great leader. Some would say it was how he treated his men. The general expected all to treat each other with honor. Others thought that it was his great strength. Some of the officers felt that the most important part of the general's leadership was that he always took responsibility. Nothing was expected from others that the general didn't expect from himself.

The subjects of leadership turned into friendly banter, soldiers laughing with each other, telling stories of battles from each one's point of view. Someone stoked the campfire and peered into the black pot, hoping to find a little more food.

The camp grew quiet, and only sparks from the campfire were heard. Everyone was lost in his own thoughts as was I. I thought about everything that had happened from the caravan journey through supper and the entire evening. As much as I wanted to stay and keep the conversation alive, I could no longer keep my eyes open.

Noticing my exhaustion, Makato motioned me to follow him and said, "Come, Shinhon, I'll show you where you will bunk tonight." As we walked, Makato stopped me and looked at me with a serious face. "One thing we did not talk about that I feel is essential in being a leader is the example you are to others. I know of no one who is a stronger example of leadership, justice, fairness and truth than General Yosha. I consider him not only my leader or commander but also my friend."

Makato began telling a story about a time when a young spy was captured. The entire encampment told Yosha that he must have this dirty spy beheaded, and Yosha listened to each man, not saying a word. He also allowed the young spy to speak as well. The spy explained that he was young and stupid. He had become a spy for money because he had grown up in poverty and often went hungry. He said that from his first memories he had no mother or father so he lived on the streets. The young man said he felt no loyalty to anyone but himself. He knew nothing of honor or love.

General Yosha saw something good in the boy. So instead of having him beheaded, he asked the spy to pledge his life to him forever. Makato said the general is the ultimate example of a leader.

Makato continued speaking with great emotion, "You see, Shinhon, I was that spy. I have never left the general's command, or side, since. His example has shown me honor and compassion. All the great people I have known demonstrate leadership by example, not words. I have heard many parents say, 'Do as I say, not as I do.' The children follow the 'as I do' regardless of what the parents say."

My mother was a shining example of a great leader I thought.

There was a strong connection between me and Makato. He showed me to a dreary looking gray tent. It contained four cots. I concluded that no one except Yosha had his own tent. Makato pointed to a cot in the back. My backpack and other belongings were already there. I was so exhausted I fell sound asleep almost before I lay down on the hard cot.

After a dreamless deep sleep, I awoke to the sounds of three snoring men. I dressed and went outside. As the sun arose, everything started turning to pink and orange. Makato was sitting in a wooden chair drinking from a steaming cup of hot brew. He spotted me and told me to grab a cup. I went to where he pointed and poured myself something hot that fired up the belly.

Makato and I sat in silence enjoying the morning brilliance; even in this desolate land everything felt new. We drank our strong drink and ate bread together. I must say I enjoyed Makato's company. I felt at peace when I was with him.

From his cup of hot drink Makato said, "General Yosha will see you today after breakfast and when you are awake." I ate the rest of my bread and finished the hot drink.

In a few minutes, I was once again knocking at Yosha's tent door. "Come!" Yosha opened the tent and I walked in, surprised to see that the great Yosha lived like his men. Thinking back to the discussion last night, I should have known his quarters would not be superior to anyone else's. While I enjoyed the symbols on his tent walls, I saw that Yosha was watching me. To break the silence I said, "The Master told me to come to you to further my education." "I know," grunted the general. He spoke sparingly. He reminded me somewhat of Old Man Chu but he was much more intimidating.

I asked him, "What do you think is the highest quality of a leader? I talked to your men last night and got many answers to my question." It felt like an eternity before he answered.

I imagined the sweet tea he sipped must be very good.

He asked me if I would like a cup of tea, as if he was reading my mind. He lifted a pot, poured out the liquid, then placed a small piece of flat bread on a plate and handed it to me. He sat back on the rickety wooden chair and continued watching me.

Finally he spoke, "You asked what qualities I believe are required to make a great leader."

I nodded.

"In order to lead in any situation one must know how to follow. He must take orders and obey them without question."

I contemplated his words. They were different than what I had expected.

"I am not sure, Yosha. I spoke with the soldiers last night, and no one mentioned following as a quality of a great leader."

He didn't appear to be that interested but asked, "What did they say?" I told him all of the qualities each officer had given and the stories that they had told, including Makato's.

Yosha sat there for a while, not speaking. I took this opportunity to indulge in the cup of sweet tea while eating a bite of the flatbread. I waited until Yosha spoke, reluctant to interrupt his thoughts.

"Shinhon!" His voice was low and commanding. "The statements you heard last night are good and valuable but the first rule of great leadership, is to be a devoted follower, willing to take orders without question, to be loyal to the leadership, and one with the troops. If he is unwilling to learn this important wisdom, a leader should be removed, for he is the weakest link."

"The greatest leaders among the men you conversed with last night are also the greatest of my followers. I would trust them to do anything, even die for me, as many have. The ultimate respect was shown to me and I do not take that lightly. I speak of respect I have earned, not because I was put in a position of leadership. Some say leaders are born but I say all people have potential to be great leaders. If they have the wisdom to follow and learn."

Yosha was quiet again. He looked at the maps on the wall of the tent.

"Like you," said the general, "I am one with the Master's army. I was, and am, a devoted follower to him. I spent many years following his guidance and directions—just like you. Master's vision of my path is different from your path. I admonish you to follow the Master, listen to the wisdom he teaches you, and practice that wisdom. I do not know what your special path is, but as you remain with him, you will do well to listen to the Master. Your path is yours and only yours. You will benefit from the Master as I did. Your life is enhanced with every wisdom that the Master imparts." He looked at me as if seeing me for the first time.

"I have been in the presence of many great men and others not worth the spit in my mouth. I see that you have the ability to be a great man someday. This world is about choices, however, and many fall short of their destiny. There is always more than one path to take. You are exceptional, Shinhon, and never forget, you were chosen."

The Device

The great general stood up from the chair.

"We are to go to the front now, to the walls of the city of Tal. It has been captured by the enemy. There is something of great importance I need to disclose to you."

The general led me out of the tent. He yelled orders for horses and quickly Makato was in front of us on his horse with two others beside him. I looked at the general's horse, a very large black stallion, as commanding a horse as the general was a man. As the general swung on to that immense animal I got the feeling that no other man could succed in riding him. It was obvious that this horse was as loyal to the general as his men were. My horse was strong and came from hardy war horse stock, but nothing compared to the general's.

We started our trek. Makato and the general were in front of me. I was keeping up as best as I could. We traveled for what seemed like hours and I was anxious, thinking about three men traveling closer to the enemy.

I began to see another tent city in the distance, with many men ready for battle. Beyond that lay a huge metropolis, with high walls of mortar and rock.

We stopped as the general looked at me and said, "This is the city of Tal. It is the outermost city north of the Master's lands. It is a link with the countries to the north. There is a lot of trading there and it has been a peaceful area until now. There is a sect of people to the far northeast called the Tundins. They are barbarians with no sense of honor."

A scowl replaced complacency on the general's face as he talked. "The enemy has taken the city of Tal. They have barricaded themselves inside. I can only assume they are waiting for reinforcements before traveling south. They have taken on the strongest state on the continent. What fools! This was a rich city and it had an abundance of provisions. They could stay in the city for a year or more and never need supplies. They have already occupied the city for months." I shook my head in understanding.

The general continued talking, "If we can take Tal back they will know the futility of their actions and the power of the tribes who support Tal—and the Master. The walls are high and there are enemies posted on the top. We would lose many men if we charged the city with ladders. Each life saved is precious."

The general looked at me with a determined face. "This is where I need your assistance, Shinhon."

I looked at the general puzzled, not understanding. "What do you mean? Your assistance?"

The general began to explain, "As you can see, this land is endowed with many large boulders. It is my plan to destroy a part of the city wall so we can charge and enter the city all at once. I sent word to the Master and asked for the best engineer in the land to build a device that would throw the huge boulders and bring down the city wall. The Master sent you to me."

I looked at him in astonishment, "Me? I am not the best engineer in all the land."

The general said, "Nevertheless, the Master sent you, and I trust the Master above all other men."

He handed me a small rock. "First, build a device that will throw this rock. We will build an even bigger one to throw those," he remarked as he pointed to the giant boulders surrounding the desolate land. "Make no mistake, young warrior, you will accomplish this feat. I have every confidence in you."

For some reason, his explanation did not make me feel better. I felt the pressure of survival of the army on my shoulders. What if I fail? I do not even know how to begin this task.

As though Yosha read my mind he said, "You will figure it out, I am sure of that. You will be given anything you need. Makato will be with you at all times. As you build, Makato will also train you to be a soldier."

The general said, "I am going to leave you now. I must tend to business. You will be here until you finish the device." He bid me and Makato goodbye and left.

"Well, soldier, how do you think we should begin? What should we do first?" asked Makato. He understood the blank look on my face and with a rather large smile he said, "How about finding our lodging and maybe a bite to eat? Then we can begin your training as a new soldier."

We found our tents and ate some food. After eating, Makato kept his word and exhibited to me the basics of battle. He then showed me fighting stances and other maneuvers. Then he explained to me that in the morning we would practice with the others. "We do many things to strengthen our body getting it ready for battle."

I told Makato of the First Wisdom and he expressed his approval and the truth behind it: Those with weak bodies will never defeat or defend.

If ever there was a good man, it was Makato, but as he taught me of battle I realized how powerful he was. I would never want to come before him in a fight.

During my sleep that night, I dreamed of constructing the device. The dream portrayed me drawing plans on a scroll, showing where every piece of the device was placed and how to assemble the wheels. Material of strong hide and ropes were necessary to hold the weapon together. In the dream, I placed each piece in perfect order.

Upon awakening, I was consumed with building the device and confident that I could engineer it. I did not think it was any more difficult than assembling a clock. I gave Makato a list of the tools and items I would need.

I worked many weeks re-creating the dream. I failed almost a hundred times. Each time the device fell before my feet. Every day I obsessed on my task. I also had my soldiers training with Makato. Even though Makato was at least 15 years my senior we became very good friends. In my mind he was the big brother I never had.

One day I arose earlier than the other men. My dream was so real I had to test it. I assembled the pieces as I remembered them. I was eager to assemble the pile of wood the way it appeared in my dream. I did not join the others for breakfast and continued working. Makato left me as he could sense I needed to concentrate all my efforts on this project. The device was completed by the end of the day. I found Makato and displayed my finished product to him.

He looked down at my tiny invention and smiled saying, "Let's use the rock that the general gave you and see if it works."

I explained the mechanics of the device. The frame supports the components and provides a raised platform from which to drop the counterweight. The counterweight, pulled by gravity alone, rotates the beam. The beam pulls the sling. The guide chute directs the sling through the frame and supports the enclosed projectile.

I set the device up and pulled the arm of the pin, flinging the rock across the camp, hitting an unsuspecting soldier hard on the side of his head. Needless to say he was quite angry. He ran toward us. Makato raised his hand to the soldier and spoke, "Thank you for helping us test the device that will probably save your life."

Realization crept into the soldier's eyes.

"You have succeeded in creating a model of the device, Shinhon." Makato laughed, "Now let's make it twenty times that size."

Later, as Makato and I ate, I did not hear the soft footsteps behind me and was surprised when General Yosha placed his massive hand on my shoulder.

"You have done well, young warrior." The general's eyes were full of light.

I told the general, "I have failed many times, but I know my device will throw a rock."

"You have never failed," the general said. "You accomplished your mission many times in discovering what did not work."

We both laughed and I understood the true lesson. It was just as Chinsha had taught me. I found out what didn't work and it led me to what did work.

I contemplated that everything in life is like this. As a child we fall many times before we walk, but the falling assists us in finding our legs.

The next day we started early on construction of the new rock throwing device. It took many soldiers under my directions to build this massive project. At the end of the construction it was quite a sight, enormous and intimidating. I had been too busy building to actually look at the machine. We all marveled at the device before us. General Yosha appeared with the rest of the men. No one spoke for a long time, walking around the device in a trance, pulling on it to ensure its strength, and examining every piece of the mechanism. He turned his attention to me, staring at me for a long while. I stared back.

Yosha roared like a lion as he spoke, "Now, let's learn how to throw a boulder because tomorrow we take back the city of Tal."

It took five soldiers to pick up a boulder to place in the device and another eight soldiers to move it any direction, and two soldiers to pull back the great arm, one notch at a time, on the counterweight. It was quite a lot of trouble.

We readied our first test and I gave my best guidance. I told the general we would send it to the trees east of the camp.

There was a notch of wood that kept the device from firing. My job was to pull the notch to engage the device.

"Ready," I yelled. Everyone made a move to squat down just a little, not knowing if this thing would explode in a thousand pieces, killing us all.

I pulled and it came loose. The counterweight gave way, coming down fast, the giant wood plank swung to the other side, and with a fast, almost instant, swish the boulder swung through and out.

All eyes looked in amazement as the boulder ascended over the trees at a great distance. Everyone was astonished at the impossibility: boulder hurled an amazing distance with what looked like ease.

The general spoke, "Good. This is very good, Shinhon. You have done well, boy, and now you are the greatest engineer in the land. Your device will guarantee our victory."

We moved the device back a lot farther and placed another boulder repeating the process. This time it completely destroyed more than five trees; shattering them into kindling.

Again, complete amazement.

Morale was high after that display. The general then made the men ready for battle, which would occur the next day. There was lots of movement. Everyone knew exactly what to do. The men were sent back to the main encampment. All the soldiers were to come back during the night, ready for battle in the morning.

We tested the device many more times, getting the aim down well.

Why Do You Fight and Kill?

I knew that tomorrow there would be death. I knew that the city had no chance once we broke through the wall and men on both sides would lose their lives.

I had done a good job of keeping my past out of my mind. But thoughts of my family came to me and I wished it was the evil warlord we were attacking. He would be nothing compared to the mighty General Yosha.

Later that night the general came to see. "We will need to aim the rock throwing weapon at the towering wall, and then, Shinhon, your job will be done. Makato and I will lead the charge through the hole created by the device."

In a humble voice I asked the general if I could speak.

"Yes, of course, what is it, Shinhon?"

I asked him, "Why do you fight and kill?"

He paused for a moment in thought and explained, "I have respect for the enemy in battle, but if not for me as a warrior to protect this land we would not be ruled by a just Master, but by the tyrants of the Tundins or other unjust individuals. I honor my land and the Master. There are two kinds of warriors, Shinhon. One lives for the blood, glory, thrill of killing, and conquest for the riches of others. Then there is the warrior who lives to protect all he loves and to mete out real justice."

"Yosha"— I called him only by his name–"I would like to fight side by side with you and Makato tomorrow. I have fallen in love with this land and the people in it. I have been taught by Makato the ways of the soldier. I would die for you tomorrow."

I saw a strange look of humility on the general's face. "Shinhon, you will fight by my side tomorrow and this I know for sure—you will not die. You still have much to learn and do. I would die tomorrow before I would let you die for me."

The night was long as we worked readying for battle. There was no sleep.

I talked with Makato about fighting with him and the general. He smiled and said, "I consider you a great friend, young Shinhon, but in battle we are brothers."

We were all dressed in new battle armor with heavy leather and strong armored jackets. There was a meeting of the commanding officers that night. The battle was planned as thoroughly as any campaign could be strategized.

Take Back the City

In the morning, as the sun started to rise in the sky, we began to move the device into position. With such a huge contraption the enemy could see us coming. It would be hard to miss. What could they do but watch? We were much too far away for arrows.

When we were in position, we stopped and set the device to ready. Many boulders were placed in carts beside the massive machine.

I can only imagine what it must have looked like to the enemy with thousands of soldiers swarming around a mysterious weapon.

The first boulder was loaded and launched high and over the wall. I could not see but assumed that there was quite a bit of damage in the city from the great rock. There was nothing the enemy could do.

We all worked together as a welloiled machine, quick to ready a new aim. The next missle hit the wall, but too high to do much damage. Just a little more adjustment and the wall was crushed, leaving a 15-foot gaping hole. The general shouted that the opening must be bigger. Time was short and the enemy would be scrambling to answer the attack.

We got quite good at loading the device. With the next boulder and the next and the next—our aim was precise, right on target. The great wall was destroyed, falling a section at a time.

"This is it," commanded the great General Yosha. He looked like a god covered in armor on his stallion. With a loud roar he began the battle chant. Makato had taught me the chant and I joined in with the same vigor as the rest.

The general's voice could be felt in the pit of your stomach and the men thundered back.

"Why do we fight?"

"To honor our fathers and the love of our mothers."

"Why do we win?"

"Freedom for our kin and land."

"And when we kill..."

"We respect the enemy whether ill or good."

"Now on to victory," the general roared in a voice loud enough to shake the enemy in their armor.

I had never felt such a rush of adrenaline. No matter what my body had been put through on Old Man Chu's, or the stables of the city of Hiin, nothing compared to this feeling.

As we ran it was clear the enemy knew they could not keep us from the city. They sent a fleet of soldiers, out of the hole in the wall, to slow us down. My only thought was to follow Yosha and Makato and stay alive.

The first collision of the two armies was maddening and somehow unreal. All that could be heard was the sound of weapons hitting armor and flesh. All reality disappeared, replaced by the will to survive.

The first thrust of the enemy was decimated in seconds. Yosha and Makato were demons of destruction.

As I passed two enemy soldiers, I swung my sword but hit metal and they were gone; no time to turn or look, there was another one before me. This time the sword met its mark, catching this man, this human; this person on the left shoulder, sinking down through the middle of his chest. I could not think about the life I had just taken, following a path of uncompromising death.

I barely noticed the swishing sound around us. Arrows came from atop of what was left of the city wall. I could see men falling but there was no opportunity to be scared or wonder if the next would be me. Just move, keep moving, kill and survive. We were at the great hole in the wall. We filed through with a mass of rage and blood. On the other side, as expected, there were many waiting for us.

Death,

So much blood and gore and no time to think.

Kill and survive.

Yosha had known that there would be archers on the city wall, so he had planned a strategy for a band of men with ladders to climb the side of the wall that was not being attacked. He knew that the bulk of the enemy would try to stop the siege at the massive hole in the wall.

As my horse and I pushed through the wall an arrow from above found its mark on my stallion. He was hit directly on the top of his head and dropped immediately to the ground. I could not breathe. I hit the ground hard but away from my steed. I arose fast, knowing that without a horse I would be a much easier target.

Kill and survive was all that mattered at that moment.

I could not think any more but only glimpse flashes of destruction and death.

I heard Yosha yelling "protect the boy."

Out of the corner of my eye I saw a huge soldier riding toward me. It was Makato, one arm outstretched to pull me onto his horse. He had a smile on his face and I realized that we were brothers in war.

An arrow came down between his shoulder blades as he reached out to me. Amazingly, he kept his balance and pulled me onto his huge stallion. Makato swung me in front of the horse and protected me with his body. He was twice my size. There was one last barrage of arrows from above. It seemed miraculous that they missed us. My massive friend and brother pushed me close to his horse.

I knew that our men had scaled the walls from the opposite side of the city and must have made it to the archers on the top walls becouse the arrows stopped. I thought for an instant about the battle atop the city. The general's men would make quick work of the archers. If we had to endure more arrows many more of us would have died.

More and more of our men engulfed the city. Many of the enemy forces began dropping their weapons, surrendering, falling to their knees. I could hear Yosha shouting out commands in an attempt to control the chaos. Almost as soon as it began it was over, a fight of no more than 20 minutes.

Soldiers shoring up what was left of the enemies. Not killing those who surrendered but taking them captive—unlike the warriors that destroyed my village. How I wished it was them we had defeated. I was certain I would show no mercy.

"It is done," Makato whispered to me.

I slid down off his horse and looked up into his eyes. With a great loving smile he said, "You are now my brother." He faltered and fell from his horse with four arrows in his back. I knew that some of them were meant for me. I knelt down before him, begging him to live. Please, there is more I need to know about being a soldier.

He did not open his eyes. I was still just a boy, not a man, and so I cried.

Warrior Farewell

I sat beside Makato's body for a long time, crying many tears. Yosha kneeled down next to me with his arm on my shoulder saying, "Makato was a great soldier and a good man. I consider him a powerful friend whom I will miss. Come, Shinhon, let us prepare the great Makato for his much deserved warrior's funeral."

The custom was that friends and platoon members were to gather the fallen and get them ready for an honorable funeral. Thoes closest to a fallen soldier would surround him with his most prized possessions and build a bonfire. His body and belongings would be set ablaze and the ashes spread over the battle ground.

Yosha ordered that the fallen enemy be gathered together as well and buried with respect and dignity.

There is much to do after battle. We worked well into the night. The enemy had not treated the people of the city very well. We assisted them as best we could. They were happy to be freed from bondage.

I could only go through the motions as I felt acute emptiness inside me. My mind pondered about all the hate and sadness in this world.

Many men gave thanks to me for building the great device that had allowed us to capture the city so easily. Many of the city people touched my hand and said "thank you" to the great engineer and soldier, Shinhon. I did not like the attention, especially now that my good friend was dead.

The bonfires of the fallen soldiers were brilliant in the night. Everyone at

Makoto's pyre had placed a stick or one of Makato's treasures on the stack. It became quite massive. As the fires were lit, one by one, they brightened the night. Looking out over the outskirts of the town I wept at the beautiful lights. I had never seen anything like it.

"I will miss you, brother," I whispered. I felt like there was a hand on my shoulder and a whisper in my ear, "I will always be with you, little brother." But I knew it was me dreaming or hallucinating from fatigue and sadness.

The fire burned for what seemed like hours and I stayed until it was a mass of coal. I did notice that Yosha was absent from the site. I am sure there was much that needed his attention.

A soldier came to me. "Master Shinhon, the general wants to see you. He is at the mayor's home in the city. I will take you there," he said.

I looked around one last time to say farewell to Makato.

No Great Spirit

As we walked through the city there was much celebrating. The soldiers were given leave to do and drink what they would, and after a heavy battle they were ready to have fun. I could hear cheers and my name yelled more than once. I also heard Makato's name mentioned with great respect.

The soldier led me up to the mayor's home. I was met by the mayor of the city.

The mayor said, "Oh great Shinhon, I thank you for your part in taking back the city. The Tundins are a hateful people." I followed him to the house where the general awaited.

I was led through the grand home and its garden setting. There in a conference room with a big table was the general discussing plans with his leaders. On the table lay a map of the city. The general and others were outlining how to strengthen the city and establish it as a stronghold so the Tundins could not vandalize it again.

No rest for the great leader, I thought, but it seemed like he could have given a little more time to mourn our friend.

When the general looked up and saw me, I could see great understanding and compassion in his eyes. He asked his men to leave.

The general and I stood alone in the room. I was still on the verge of tears. The general spoke first. "Thank you, Shinhon. Many lives were saved today because of your incredible device."

With tears in my eyes, I said, "I really don't feel like celebrating, General.

Makato was an excellent man and he saved my life."

The General came up to me putting his hand on my shoulder and spoke. "The greatest honor of a warrior is to save the life of a brother in battle. The Great Spirit will reward Makato, of this you can be sure."

I looked at Yosha with a sad face and told him I did not believe in the Great Spirit.

"I have a strong belief in the Great Spirit; the world is a wondrous place. Have you ever thought about death?" Yosha asked.

"Yes, I have. Death has been an inescapable part of me since my family, along with our entire village, was destroyed by the warlord Udoki. I know death is a sad and horrible thing. I know what it is to lose loved ones. I carry this burden every single day of my life. Now there is another death to carry around in my heart, making it even heavier. No. I believe there is nothing after life, only death."

The general said, "Death is as natural as life. We are born and it is a beautiful thing to see a child come into this world. Everyone celebrates the newborn, but no one celebrates death. Sometimes I think the clan of Shu has the idea of birth and death accurately. The Shu find great joy in celebrating the death of loved ones. They are happy the person's work is finished in the land of physical reality. To the Shu death is not a time of mourning but a time of joy and happiness. They believe their loved ones are going into the next life with the Great Spirit. I understand that you do not believe in the Great Spirit, but many find comfort in their belief."

I replied in an irritated voice, "That's right, General Yosha. The Great Spirit is a wish, a hope people have to comfort themselves."

He asked, "If there is no Great Spirit, then what holds us together?"

"We do," I said in a voice much harsher than I meant. "It is up to each and every one of us to live a good life, and when it is finished disappear into nothingness."

He asked, "And how do you know what a good life is?"

I explained, "Because I can feel what is good and what is bad. I know that it is not noble to kill another for greed or jealousy, or to steal another's property. If I tell a lie, it hurts my heart, so I know for sure that it is not the worthy thing to do."

He asked, "So, young Shinhon, if that is what you feel when you do what you sense is right or wrong, where do you believe the feelings come from?"

I answered with doubt in my voice, "Training from my family, my mother for sure, and my own perception."

He countered, "Your parents can only teach you so much. It is your inner soul that guides and teaches you throughout your life on this earth. Why do you think this is? Why would your soul need improving if it is merely going to disappear? Our thoughts will only take us so far, get us through day to day activity. It is our heart or inner soul that allows us to have feelings and know the difference between good and corrupt. So, even if there is no Great Spirit, will you at least consider that you yourself may have a spirit or soul and that the energy of your life and the life you have lived on earth may live after death?"

The general continued, "A man builds a great house and if he is a good builder who builds his home with the finest, hardiest materials, it might stand secure for thousands of years, and the energy of this man lives on in the house. It is felt by everyone who visits or lives there afterward."

He paused for a moment, "Makato has left a path of good energy since the time he was caught as a spy. His energy will live on and I believe that he is beside the Great Spirit.

We stood in silence thinking about Makato. Then the general spoke, "We are all under enchantment before birth, and all humans, including animals and insects have a fear of death. This fear is strong and for most living things is the ultimate fear. Animals have a natural instinct and will do anything to stay alive. I have seen them react to pending death. Their instincts guide them to build nests away from the enemy. Great fear is seen in an animal's eyes when it tries to flee from hunters.

"Shinhon, true enlightenment in this world comes to those who are not afraid to die. They place little significance in death when their time comes. They know for sure death will come to them, but it does not raise fear. They live their lives fully, as death is only another part of life.

"Death will be one of two things. Either you will go on in spirit to the next level of learning or you will have the most peaceful sleep for eternity.

"The Master sees something great in you, Shinhon. I see it as well. You will learn what special gifts have been given to you in life. No one can find them for you, or force you to learn anything that does not connect with you.

"Celebrate Makato, he deserves that. I loved him as if he were my son."

Tears ran down my face as I began to understand Yosha and I felt better about life and death. Just in that instant I comprehended a new level of learning.

"The greatest thing you can do for Makato," Yosha said, "is to remember him and emulate his life."

"I will," I said, looking up at the man before me. His eyes said more than I could explain. There was sadness, joy, love, anger, and hate all rolled into one powerful emotion. I could see that he had taken the message to heart for himself and lived a life of learning. It is good to have great people in your life. I was thankful for my relationship with the general.

The Vagabond

"It is time for you to find your destiny, my boy," Yosha said rather abruptly.

"Go? You mean leave?" I questioned.

"Yes," he said "there is a man down the hall waiting to take you back to the palace of the Master."

There was a slight smile on his face.

"I don't know that I have learned all I can from you, General Yosha."

"The world turns and everything happens for a reason," the great General Yosha said. "You will see, dear boy. Enjoy the journey and treasure the wisdom you gain each day. Above all, stay curious."

He reached down and picked up my little talisman. "I see you have the symbol for 'four' around your neck."

I looked down at my amulet. "Yes it was given to me by the great merchant Chinsha's daughter. Does it have meaning?" I asked him.

"Maybe on your journey you will find out what it means. I do not have time to talk more but I would give you an embrace. I will give you a 'four' now if you would permit me."

I looked at him not understanding. He opened his arms and grabbed me. Yosha was a strong man. I saw firsthand the great strength he had with a sword, but, this was the gentle hug of a father. I hugged him back, long and hard. I would miss this great man.

He told me to go down the hall and meet with the man who would assist me in continuing my journey. I said good bye one last time. He grabbed both my arms and smiled. I followed his instruction and began down the hall.

Yosha shouted for his officers to come and continue their work.

I walked down the hall for what seemed like a long time. Soon the voices of the general and his men faded, becoming whispers instead of loud banter. I came to an area that crossed another hall, and then a large double door opened. There I saw a man sitting in a decorated purple and gold ornate chair. There was something strange about his looks.

I wondered who he was and what he was doing. He smelled bad and looked like a filthy vagrant. His appearance was that of a beggar. But, through the filth and nastiness, his soft blue eyes glistened. They were beautiful and knowledgeable.

The nasty beggar stood and spoke, "Hello, friend. You are the mighty Shinhon who assisted the general in taking back the great city of Tal from despicable bandits. You will become legend and there will be discussions of this venture and your invention for many years to come."

His voice sounded familiar. I wondered if this was the man General Yosha wanted me to travel with.

"Here is some clothing for the journey. You will be traveling with me and you cannot wear soldier's clothing." He handed me a pile of rags. They did not smell much better than he did. "We will travel for some time with an empty caravan until we get out of the wastelands. Then it will only be you and me."

I looked at the man and the rags he was wearing. It seemed strange that he would have been sent to me. Even stranger was the fact that a beggar, someone of little consequence, was talking to me like an equal. I had proven myself and I felt I deserved better than to be escorted by a common vagabond.

I thought of the 310 gold pieces I had earned with the merchant, Chinsha and was careful to keep them safe and well hidden. I said, "There are many merchants in the city and I am wealthy. I can buy my own clothes."

"No," said the beggar. "We travel as we are."

"Why must we wear these smelly rags? There is no reason to travel like this."

The beggar said with a smile, "This is how we travel."

I was disgusted with the rags but it was nice to take off my blood splattered uniform.

The old man said, "The caravan is ready to leave tonight and they are anxious to get on the road as soon as possible. Many of the men have been locked in the city, captive for some time, and are ready to see loved ones and take care of other business. We will go with the caravan until we get to the farm lands and beg our way through to the city of Hiin. Then we go to the Master's palace."

What could I possibly learn from this stupid old beggar? I thought. I could have made it to the Master on my own. I knew the way and I was sure I could defend myself.

The beggar took nothing with him except a small bag. I had no idea what was in it. I had my bag of essential items and my gold tucked safely away.

He looked around and whispered, "Let's go now." I followed the beggar out of the house, and we went to the part of the city where the caravan was preparing to leave. The beggar kneeled down and picked up a handful of dirt. Before I knew what had happened, he smeared dirt in my face.

"A poor peasant beggar does not have a clean face or hands. You must not be recognized. You have obtained quite a name for yourself . The people have been shouting hurrahs for the great Shinhon."

"I do not feel that I did anything special," I said. "Anyone with a logical mind could have built the device just as well or maybe better than I."

"Humility is a good thing in life," the beggar said. "Modesty can keep you from being deceived."

I questioned him. "Deceived about what and from whom?"

"Deceived by you about yourself," the beggar laughed.

We made it to the caravan without being noticed. The beggar explained our plight to the caravan leader and with some reluctance we were allowed to travel with the caravan. One beggar was bad enough, but two?

They were ready to get started that night and planned to travel only a few miles out of the city. Then we would camp and get a fresh start in the morning. I was starving by the time we left. I had not slept for two days and my eyes only wanted to close. I was informed that the men were willing to share the night's meal with us.

This caravan was no better than the last. We were given the worst of the scraps for food. It was quite amusing the way some of the men would sneer at me and the beggar. At supper they talked of the great Shinhon who, side by side with the great General Yosha had taken back the city and released the people from bondage. Some would make up stories saying they were his close friend. I had a smile on my face. I had never seen them before.

Soon, we passed small cities and isolated farm houses. The caravan stopped at one small city. The beggar told me it was time for us to part company with the caravan. I was excited to be on our own. The caravan drivers gave us some food and we packed it away. It was not much but would keep us alive for a short time.

We walked for days. The beggar was not much of a talker but he did have a kind and wise quality about him.

Rich Farm

One night we came upon a great farm house. It was very luxurious. There were many servants working hard. The beggar asked about lodging but no one spoke. Finally one of the servants said, "You will have to speak with the master of the farm at the big house."

We picked up our pack and went to the main farm house. It was getting late and wonderful aromas came from the kitchen where the evening meal was being prepared. We knocked on the door and waited a long time. A man opened the door and looked us up and down, making a face as though he was disgusted with what he was looking at.

"What do you want?" he asked as he narrowed the door so we could barely see him. With a bitter voice, he said, "Beggars, go away! I have nothing for you here, just go away!"

The old beggar spoke. "Sir, we have traveled far and only ask for a place to spend the night."

He opened the door with a scowl on his face saying, "I don't care what you need, even if you are starving—it means nothing to me. Get away from my door and my grounds. I have important business and do not have time to waste on the likes of you."

The old beggar pleaded, "Please, master, is there any place we could stay, just for the night? I promise we will be no trouble."

The farm master looked us up and down again and told us if we would leave his presence, he was willing to let us stay in his small cellar in the back of the house. He told us that the door was open. He said we could stay in the cellar for the night but if anything was stolen or in disarray in any way, he would have us hunted down and strung from the highest tree. "Now go, get out of my sight. I want you gone before I awake in the morning." With that, he slammed the door.

"He was not a nice man, not a nice man at all." I said. The beggar smiled. "Yes, he believes he is important."

We got to the cellar. I thought it would have been better to sleep under the stars. It was obvious the cellar had not been used in a long time. It looked as though it housed only spider webs and rat's nests. We found an ancient lantern and were able to light it with some flint the beggar had tucked away. Then, we "enjoyed" a humble dinner of roots and berries that we had found in our travels.

I told the old beggar it was sad that a man who had so much could offer so little. He seemed cold, bitter, and unhappy to me. The rich man could have given us a good meal and a nice place to stay but we were just beggars to him and not worthy of his hospitality.

"You do not know a man until you walk in his shoes," replied the beggar as he popped a berry into his mouth. "Maybe he has been beaten and robbed by beggars and still carries that memory and trusts no one."

I shrugged. "Still, he didn't have to treat us in such a shabby manner."

My companion looked at me. "You will learn throughout your life that people carry memories deep within and act upon them without knowing why. We all do until we realize that it was in the past and is irrelevant now. Sometimes it takes a life time of pain to realize this, and some never do."

I thought to myself, I am not a beggar. If only he knew who I was he would have treated us differently.

After our tiny meal the beggar got up and said there was something he must do. There were some tools in the cellar. I watched as the beggar got a bucket and began putting some things into it. He then left for a moment and returned with some water.

What is he doing?

He began mixing something up in the bucket.

"What are you doing?" I asked. I thought he was crazy.

"Mixing some plaster to blend with water."

"Plaster for what?"

As he pointed he said, "See the wall over there? It is worn and cracked and has a small hole in it. I am going to fix it."

"What? Why would you fix anything for someone who gave us next to nothing? That man has many servants and people who could fix this wall so why should you fix it for him?" What was the beggar thinking? In my mind, he was being kind to someone who really did not deserve it.

"I am aware of what the man has, but I will do it anyway," the old beggar said. I watched as he took great pains to fix the wall. I fell asleep before he was finished. In the morning the beggar woke me early saying, "We must be on our way."

I looked at the wall. "You should be a wall maker and not a beggar. This wall looks amazing; perfect, like there was never a crack or hole in it. Did you take all night?"

"I slept some," he said.

We left before anyone on the farm stirred.

I was glad to leave that place, all that wealth and no gratitude. At least now he has a nice wall in a nasty cellar. I think the beggar may be a little crazy.

I asked him, "Why?"

"Why what?" he said.

"Why fix that ungrateful person's wall? He will probably never see it anyway. I think it was stupid that you worked so hard for half the night."

"I worked on it even more than half the night. If you're going to do something you should give it your all," the beggar said. "I will just tell you that things are not always what they seem."

"What did you mean? Not what they seem? You helped someone who did not want or need your help. It seems pretty pointless to me."

Poor Farm

We traveled a long time and found some shelter for the night. We had a small helping of food and some berries we had found, but we were running out of supplies.

The next day we started early in the morning. Sometime after mid-day we came upon another farm which was much different than the farm we left. There were no servants, no gardeners, only a humble-looking dilapidated farm. It was quite rundown. I didn't see much livestock, only one old cow that did not look so healthy.

We went up to a door that looked as though it had not been repaired in many years.

A man and woman came to the door. "Hello," they both said in unison with the brightest, happiest smiles on their faces. "Welcome, weary travelers. Please come in and make yourselves at home. You look as though you have traveled long and hard."

"We have come from the city of Tal. We are grateful for your hospitality." The beggar said as he bowed low to our hosts. They both bowed back.

"Oh my goodness," the woman said as she told us to come in and sit. The woman said that they had heard of the great battle in Tal. The man added that he heard there was a boy, a great engineer and warrior, who had defeated the vandals with a marvelous instrument. The boy's name was Shinhon, rumored to be the Master's pupil. If the Tundins had not been stopped at the north they would eventually have taken every city captive.

Hadi and Hin were a sweet couple and it was obvious that they loved each other very much. Hin told us that this farm had been in his family for many generations and that he and Hadi had been working it for thirty years.

As they prepared dinner for us, I couldn't help but admire them, bustling about the kitchen, laughing and stopping only to kiss each other. They placed the humble, but delicious, food on the table. They were anxious to talk and tell us about their lives together. The children were grown and gone and had families of their own. When they told us how rich their lives were together, I felt a deep pain as I thought again of my family. They asked us to stay for the night.

"You may have our bed in the loft upstairs," said Hadi. "We will sleep on the floor of the main room." We protested, but they insisted that we take their bed and explained that they were comfortable sleeping on the floor as that is what they did when their children and grandchildren came to visit. They piled several blankets and two pillows on the floor for themselves. Compared to what we were used to the bed in the loft was wonderful, like sleeping on a cloud.

Hadi and Hin were such good people, so different from the crabby, wealthy, bitter farmer we had stayed with the night before. The old beggar went to sleep early. Before I went to sleep I thought that there were plenty of cracked walls in this house. This couple could use some assistance. I retired after talking with Hadi and Hin. I fell asleep as soon as my head hit the pillow and slept well.

I was awakened by the beggar early the next morning—the sun had not yet risen. "What is going on?" I asked him. The beggar explained we had a long way to go and needed to get started. Hadi and Hin had given us provisions, which I knew they could not afford.

We had already packed and were quiet so we would not wake the couple as we left.

Things Are Not Always What They Seem

We got outside and as I started down the path to leave the farm traveling south I looked back and there was the beggar putting a rope around the neck of the cow. I could not believe my eyes. He opened the gate and led the old cow through.

I asked him what he was doing as he walked up to me with the old animal.

"I am taking this cow," he said with no emotion in his voice.

Feeling angry I said, "We cannot take this cow! It is almost all they have except for a few chickens."

"Yes we can and that is what I am doing." He replied. "I ask you to say no more about this. We must leave this farm before the good Hadi and Hin wake up."

I thought maybe I had been tricked by a crafty old swindler and had met with the wrong man at the mayor's house in Tal. I had not verified with General Yosha that this was the man I was supposed to meet.

As if the beggar read my mind he said, "I am the person you are supposed to be with and things are not always what they seem."

In answer to his statement I said, "You are stealing their livestock. It looks only one way to me."

He said softly, "You must trust me." His eyes showed only goodness in them. My urge to run to the house and wake up Hadi and Hin left and I gave up and walked with him.

We walked for many hours. The old man was pushing us hard to go fast. A few hours later he said to follow him as he led the cow off the path and down into a dry creek bed. I followed and then we walked for some time. We stopped as the creek widened. It was still dry but bigger.

"This is a good spot," the old man said.

The old man reached·down and picked up a large rock. The rock was almost too heavy for him to lift. With great force, more than I believed him capable of, he brought the rock down hard, opening the old cow's head. The cow dropped from the force, twitching and jerking its legs, while it writhed on the ground. I watched in horror.

The twitching soon stopped and the cow lay motionless.

I felt numb. I knew for sure I had met the wrong man and was now traveling with a lunatic who would soon smash my head with that same rock.

I looked at the man's soft eyes. He did not look crazy. He must have seen my horror because he said, "Shinhon, things are not always what they seem. In life, people make judgments prematurely.

I yelled in astonishment, "I know that you helped the rich farmer who needed nothing and destroyed the livelihood of a poor farm family who had nothing. There is no other way I can see it. I don't think you are the man I was supposed to meet at the city of Tal. You would probably bludgeon me in my sleep. Maybe you are one of the barbarians and are going to take your revenge out on me."

The old man looked at me with tenderness in his eyes. "Are you sure that is the only way to see it?"

The man continued to speak. "When we came to the farm of the wealthy man, I felt his energy, and knew that he had spent his entire existence creating wealth, but had missed life. Wealth is his whole ambition and he created much of it, paying no attention to the life he was entitled to. I did not judge him but knew he had more wealth than he needed, and that was all he wanted in life. That is why I fixed the wall in his cellar."

Confused, I said, "What do you mean? I do not understand you at all."

"When we first went into the cellar I noticed the holes in the wall. I also noticed that everything was in disrepair. I have learned to pay attention to my surroundings. I looked into the cracks on the wall that had been decaying little by little over the years. Soon the wall would open even more and crumble at some point. I noticed that inside the wall was a great treasure. I could not be sure how much, but I can say that it was substantial, maybe even more then all of this man's riches. And so, knowing that he had more wealth than he could ever use in a lifetime, I made it so the secret of the treasure would stay in the wall."

What? I was amazed. A huge treasure sealed in the wall! I contemplated this for some time. The man was silent and let me ponder over his message.

"But what of this?" I asked, pointing to the dead cow. "I see no reason to steal the good people's cow and kill it in the middle of nowhere. This makes no sense to me at all."

"Look," said the man. He walked over and bent down pulling up on the eyelid of the dead animal. "See the black around the edge of the animal's eye? This is the beginning of a deadly disease. If anyone were to eat this cow they would die an agonizing death. The animal is still in the beginning stages of the disease and the milk that it gives is not yet infected. But in time it would have passed the sickness on to the good people in the farm we left."

He then told me, "I took the liberty of taking the gold you had. I left it for Hadi and Hin. I am sure you will earn more. The 310 gold pieces will buy the couple much more than another cow. They will be able to live comfortably for the rest of their days."

In that instant I was struck by a strong discovery. I had always looked at life in a simple way. I just realized life was fuller, and more beautiful then I had ever realized. I had new eyes to see reality and as I looked at the old man, he changed.

"Master?" I whispered under my breath.

Why did I not see this before? He did not disguise his face or mask himself. The only difference was the clothing he wore.

Stunned, I asked, "Master, how did I not know it was you?"

He said, "The real question is, how did you recognize me now?"

I guess in that instant I realized I was looking at the world in a shallow, simple way, and in the instant, I realized there were many other possibilities. The world was different from the way I had been looking at it. It was then that I just saw you."

"Very good," he said. "We must get on the road, but first we must cover this beast with rocks. It would not be good if any living thing ate it."

It took some time to cover the animal, and soon we were on the road, traveling once again.

Learning

It took many more days to reach the palace. It had been a long journey but a beautiful one. I looked at the world differently and could not believe the joy this new discovery brought to me.

I thought of my family and remembered the love and happiness we had together. I thought of the great man Makato. The horror of those happenings lessened.

The people we met were beautiful, each in their own way. I saw everything through different eyes.

When we got to the palace I felt like life was good and worth living. Being with the Master for this time was most enlightening. I got to know him as a man but still it seemed impossible to know his deepest self.

The Master told me to get some good rest and meet him in the great hall tomorrow so we could talk about the wisdom I had learned.

The palace was wonderful. It seemed like years since I had been there. I found it uncomfortable on such a soft bed, but I was weary from the journey so I slept well.

In the morning I was called to the great hall. I stood there in front of the Master.

"You have been gone for some time, Shinhon. Tell me all you have learned of this Second Wisdom. Tell me everything."

I thought about everything from the day I left the palace until now.

"Master, this is the Wisdom of Learning. I have learned so much.

Merchant Chinsha and General Yosha were teachers of the highest caliber. I have learned that it is to my advantage to listen and learn from everything and everyone around me."

Master you say there are Eight Wisdoms, but I cannot see how there can be any more? I believe that as we learn, and understand what we learn, anything is possible. I have heard the question asked many times. What is the meaning of life? I believe the answer to that question is to learn."

The Master spoke, "The wisdom of learning is important to everyone in life. Always being open to learn new wisdom is important, but along with the Wisdom of Learning you will see deeper and be open to the other wisdoms. Knowledge is a tricky thing. There are many in the world who possess much knowledge, yet have little wisdom. They believe there is wisdom only in books or in learning from a leader.

It is like the man who says, "I know this snake is deadly but I will play with it because it is fun. He has the knowledge of danger but not the wisdom to leave it alone."

I nodded my head in agreement.

"Shinhon, you have done well. I ask that you pay close attention to the difference between knowledge and wisdom."

He stood up and put his hand on my shoulder, "Wisdom is learned and driven by your spirit and knowledge by your mind."

WISDOM

3

"*My religion consists of a humble admiration of the illimitable superior spirit who reveals himself in the slight details we are able to perceive with our frail and feeble mind.*"

ALBERT EINSTEIN

A Message

"We know now that wisdom is learned and driven by your spirit and knowledge by your mind." The words kept running through my thoughts, over and over. I knew I had obtained a great deal of knowledge in the time that I worked on the first two wisdoms, and was satisfied with the success I had gained. But,wisdom? Something about the meaning of the words touched my soul.

The Master said, "You have done well for the first two wisdoms. I am proud of your tenacity to learn. Tomorrow you will start on a new journey."

"What do you know of the Great Spirit?" asked the Master.

I thought about the question for a moment and said, "Master, my parents believed in the Great Spirit and taught me what was in their heart about the Great Unknown, but I cannot believe there is 'something' good out there that allows all the horrifying disasters and unhappiness in this world. I know if something bad happens in my life, it is up to me to take care of it. I rule my own destiny by the everyday choices I make. I do not believe that there is a Great Spirit who guides the purpose of my life."

He looked at me for a long time as though he was digesting the words I said to him. His facial expressions did not change. "This is your next task, Shinhon. You are to go to the south desert and will need provisions for keeping cool. It is hot and you must wear clothing that will cover your body and head. You must take as much water as you can carry. On the other side of the desert there is a Temple nestled in the mountains above a small city. You will be given a map to make sure you have the correct directions.

"A priest named Laotzu lives at the temple. You are to tell him that you have a message from The Master. Tell him that you are my apprentice, and you feel that there is no Great Spirit and as my apprentice you were to decide the fate of the Temple. Tell him to do whatever you wish with the Temple. You can close it down or do what you feel is the right thing to do."

I couldn't believe my ears. A tingle of excitement spread through my body.

With a twinkle in his eyes the Master looked deep into mine and asked, "Are you ready to start your training?"

"Yes, Master," I said.

I thought I had already started. I have learned to listen to the Master with a more open mind. I knew he was saying that every day was a new life and a new chance to learn. I was learning his methods.

"Take as many provisions as you think you will need, but keep in mind that the journey across the desert is a treacherous one."

"Master," I asked, "Is this expedition more treacherous than the voyages I've already endured?"

The Master had a serious look on his face and said, "Know that the desert is deadly. Get a good night's rest, young Shinhon, and begin your newest adventure in the morning."

I spent some time stuffing everything I thought I would need in my backpack. I had heard stories from others in the palace of the great desert. Many people attempted to cross the desert and never returned. I packed as much food and water as I could carry. I slept well in the palace that night and was off on my journey the next day. The edge of the desert was not far from the palace. The desert protected the Masters, stronghold. It would be hard for an enemy to attack from the sandy region without being heard or seen.

The Desert

The next day turned out to be pleasant and balmy. I smiled to myself at the influence I seemed to have on the Master. I felt he believed me when I said that there was no such thing as a Great Spirit. I was to inform the priest to do whatever I felt appropriate with the temple. I thought maybe the temple could be used as a great market place or a museum for modern thought.

I learned the journey would not be easy—not easy at all. The sun continued to be bright, even at daybreak and twilight. I was grateful for the covering that I had brought to shield my head. I did not know how long it would take me to cross the desert, but I did hear from others it could take up to a month on foot. I was given a map. The map turned out to be very valuable because there were many refugee oases where I could resupply my foodstuff and water.

The first day in the desert was difficult. I was grateful for being in good physical condition. I exercised my body as much as possible during the day and ate good food. I believed—now I knew why the Wisdom of the Physical was so important in life. I noticed that I was drinking lots of water and that I needed to ration my supplies if they were going to last.

At the end of the first week I knew that the Master did not exaggerate when he said this was a difficult trip. I think he understated the struggle of the desert. My water was running out. I found that reading the map was not quite as easy as I thought it would be. On the eighth day, my water reserve ran out—I knew I was in trouble. For many days the sun was scalding hot.

I was blistered and burned, even though I wore clothes for protection. The nights were freezing cold. The changes in the climate were brutal.

On the ninth day and now no water, I believed I would die. My mouth was as dry as the sand I had walked through and I felt all fluids drain from my body. I could not walk any longer and was too weak to move. Why did the Master send me to this terrible place?

On the eleventh day, I tried to crawl but didn't get far. My body was drained. I saw vultures flying over my head watching me. I was surely dead and had given up hope. I quit trying to understand the map. I cursed the Master's deceit.

On the twelfth day I was convinced he was trying to kill me. After all I had been through he sent me here to die in the desert alone. I caught a glimpse of his face in my mind and I hated him, because I had believed in him. I was a fool. Then, my thoughts turned to my time with him in the farmland to the north. Things are not always what they seem to be I remembered. I knew then there had to be some good explanation, some lesson to learn.

I knew I was dying and without water I would be dead by tomorrow. I felt death deep in my aching body. I understood how unkind this world could be. As I lay down to die, I was certain that there was nothing more I could do.

At that point of deepest despair a voice came to me. I thought it was an illusion. The voice was not loud but clear and distinctive.

"There is life to the left on the other side of the hill, Shinhon." I dismissed it as hallucination. Again, the voice spoke, "There is life to the left on the other side of that sand dune."

Hallucination or not it gave me something to do before I died. With all my strength, I crawled, inch by inch, over the top of the hill. It seemed to take forever, but I got to the top.

At the top of the dune, I looked down thinking I would only see more desert. There stood an oasis in the middle of the desolation. The oasis was not very big, but there were several trees and a small bubbling pond. The pond must have been fed by an underground stream.

Painfully, I crawled down the other side of the hill. My body was aching and I knew that I must be close to death. Going down the dune was easier than going up. The vision of the water gave me a kind of reverie. My mind raced as I thought of how many of us would give up when life was just around the corner or over the hill.

I crawled up to the water's edge and gulped it down. Then, without removing my clothes, I crawled into the pond. The life resurrection of the cool clear water was unbelievable. I lay in the water for what seemed like hours. I noticed little brown objects on one of the trees. I decided to explore and discovered they were delicious dates.

I remained at the oasis for many days, regaining my strength. I had forgotten about the voice—the voice that saved my life. I thought it was of no consequence, and only how lucky I was to find this place. I shuddered as I realized how close I had been to death when there was life right over the hill.

My father had taught me well how to build traps for catching food. He also taught me survival techniques as well as which fruits were good for eating and which were poisonous. This was the only water for miles and there was an overabundance of small animals that I was able to catch for food.

After what must have been many days of healing I knew I needed to keep going. I realized that the temple was to the south and I followed the map as I continued on my journey.

I loaded as much water in my water satchel as I could. I also picked many dates and stuffed them into my bag. I proceeded to pack what little meat I was able to catch. I knew that I wouldn't last long traveling with these small supplies, but I had no choice. With a new reserve of energy and vigor. I kept going toward the south. After a few days I began to lose all hope again. I could see mountains in the distance. That had to be where the temple was located. It could be weeks away for all I knew.

Many days passed and with each day I felt the aching in my bones and sore muscles. My water supply was running low again and I knew that I would not live unless I found another water reservoir. I kept going, not daring to stop any more than I had to. The nights were so cold that I felt I would freeze to death, then the day would come and the sun's heat would burn until I could not breathe.

I rationed my water, but my supply was depleted, death was close again—I knew it. I knew that I would not last much longer without water. But I just kept walking. My mind was muddled and I could not think straight. By day, I hallucinated, seeing oases' everywhere—and when I ran to where they appeared to be they disappeared. All I could do at night was wrap myself up in my blankets and sleep. I experienced horrible nightmares. I saw snakes and scorpions everywhere on my body, munching on what was left of me.

Why didn't the Master just have me killed? He had many chances. Why did he send me to the desert to die? I had seen nothing in this man but goodness.

My thoughts turned to myself, the great Shinhon, engineer and brave soldier of General Yosha, dead alone in a desolate desert. No one on earth would miss me. Even the Master had deserted me. What had I done to deserve this torturous death? I did my best to see the world differently but in my mind I knew there was no hope. I was going to die. My last lesson would be learning how to die. I laughed like I had gone mad and could not help myself.

I was no longer able to walk so I lay on the sand, fatigued beyond reason. I was ready to give up. In and out of consciousness all night, I no longer had the strength to feel anything but sorrow and betrayal.

Time was lost to me. I was lost.

From the deep despair I felt, I heard a familiar voice. A voice I had heard many times. I didn't listen to the hallucination. I heard the soft voice again. It was my mother's voice, coaxing me to listen to her. I knew death must be close now. I thought of her spirit living on as Yosha had told me. I loved and missed her so much. It was then that I began to cry.

My mother's soft voice told me that I would not die. The Great Spirit had sent her to give me a message of comfort.

I mumbled back, "I do not believe in the Great Spirit."

Her voice whispered, "He believes in you."

I said to the personage in a quiet whisper, "If there is a Divine Being who cares about us, this world would not be a place of suffering."

"I love you, my son," her voice said. "The greatest spirits in mortal form that live on earth experience sorrow and sadness, and often serious physical pain, to assist them in learning important body and soul lessons. This seems harsh, but it catapults life's learning. It is a choice to see life as bad or good no matter what you experience."

I wiped my eyes. I didn't know if this was a cruel joke of the mind or if she was really talking to me?

She continued, "You are alive at this time to experience what your spirit is capable of and to choose how you will accept that knowledge. Knowing how you feel about the sorrows and suffering people experience in life is one step closer to being enlightened. My Shinhon, I have always known that you were special."

"I am going to die and there is no hope," I said.

Her gentle voice replied, "You will not die as it is not your time."

I could not move. I wanted to go away with my mother; I wanted the pain and grief to stop.

"Shinhon," The sweet voice of my mother said, "Use all the strength in your body. There is a stick beside you. It is there, you just have to reach for it. Put the stick in the ground and tie your shirt around the stick."

I could not move, still I felt a gentle power pulling me upward. It was like a sweet breeze from my mother's breath.

"I am sad." I stated, "Maybe it would be better to die and be with you?"

"No," my mother said. "You have much more to learn about this world."

Waves of power rippled throughout my body, my muscles felt the force. It was as if a lightning bolt had hit me. I picked up the stick and tied the shirt around it. I dropped to the ground like a sack of grain. Blessed darkness enfolded me. I felt warm, safe and loved but I still did not understand.

The Temple and Questions

I don't know how many days passed, but I awoke in a cart in a camel caravan. One of the caravan drivers yelled back at me, "About time you woke up boy. We are almost to the village under the temple. Are you feeling all right?"

"Yes, I am fine," I told him with feelings of despair. I felt like the entire caravan had run over my body.

Within seconds, a man appeared. He dropped a little water to my lips wetting them.

"Don't drink too fast, you'll get sick." He smiled at me. I asked him what had happened and how I had managed to be in the caravan. He told me that I was lucky to be alive. He explained that a boy on the caravan had wandered off to explore. The boy saw the stick and the flag waving in the wind of the day. Curious, he walked over to see why there was a shirt on a stick in the middle of nowhere and that was where he discovered me. At first he thought I was dead. The vultures were close by. He discovered that I was close to death but not dead yet.

The kind man said, "The boy came back to the caravan and told us about you. Then he lead us to where you were laying and we gave you water. You were delirious and babbled on about the Great Spirit and spoke of your mother. You wanted to be with her. You were begging to leave your broken body here. We are only two days from the village of the great temple. You will be able to regain your strength there."

I was weak and slept most of the two-day journey to the village. People asked me who I was, where I was going, and why I was crossing the desert alone? I told them my name was Shinhon and I was directed to give a message from the Master to the priest of the temple.

"You are the great Shinhon?" A man asked in surprise. He told me how much of an honor it was to be in the presence of a pupil of the Master. They had heard I left on my journey many months before. I wondered if that could be true, but I was too tired to argue.

He spoke again, "You were feared dead. You must be immortal to survive months in the desert."

I told them they must be wrong. I was only in the desert a few weeks.

I told them, "I am only a man."

They knew the message to the priest must be important and they felt the reason they had found me was because the Great Spirit had directed and guided them. I didn't want to think about it. I was too weak and my head was pounding with pain.

After entering the city I was taken directly to the temple. The caravan people wanted me to deliver my message.

After leaving the harshness of the desert, the village and temple were a beautiful transition from the heat and cold. The village seemed like a beautiful oasis. The city lay nestled at the bottom of the mountains. The temple was striking and could be seen clearly in all its glory, far up the side of the mountains. There were farms and cattle on the mountain side. I was taken to the top of a road that led to the temple. I was able to get up from the cot the caravan drivers had prepared for me. The leader of the procession went up to the massive door first. A woman, covered in robes from her head to her feet answered the door. She bowed to the driver. I saw him pointing to where I stood and heard him say to her, "The great Shinhon, apprentice to the Master, has come a long way to deliver a message from the Master to the priest, Laotzu."

She left and was gone for a short time. The door opened again and she motioned for me to come in. I was slow but able to walk on my own. When I got to the door the men bowed low and bid me farewell.

The woman bowed to me and I bowed back as best I could. She raised her hand, beckoning me to follow her. I followed her down the long hallway through the temple. What a magnificent place; so very beautiful, but still unpretentious. I also noticed to my amazement that I felt stronger, healed by the temple's energy. I actually felt well. The woman took me to the door of a large room. It was peaceful, with colorful canvases on the wall. In the middle of the room there stood an altar. I felt myself grow stronger by the minute just being there. A man in white and gold robes was kneeling at the colossal altar in deep meditation. There was a peaceful look on his face. The energy in the room was so intense that I did not want to make noise or disturb the peacefulness of this place.

After a few minutes, and without looking up, the priest said, "You have a message for me, Shinhon. Come closer, and sit. I am Laotzu, the priest you seek. I have been expecting you."

How could he be expecting me?

I was struck with an urge to talk and began to explain myself. "Laotzu, the Master taught me to learn the wisdoms of life. At the beginning of my journey to your temple, The Master asked me how I felt about the Great Spirit. I told him that I did not believe there was a Great Spirit. The Master instructed me to tell you that there is no Great Spirit and also that I could do whatever I felt appropriate with the temple."

I paused and bowed my head as I said, "I cannot tell you there is no Great Spirit. After my journey in the desert I am now confused and believe that there may be something beyond my comprehension. I do not understand the world, nor do I understand the ways of the spirits. I do know there is more to this life; I just do not understand it."

Laotzu spoke, "Knowledge is sometimes a trick that binds us to the philosophy of man."

I looked into the eyes of this gentle man and felt at home, moreover, I felt safe and protected. "May I stay with you and learn of this other world?" I asked him.

"Yes, of course," said Laotzu.

Symbol of the Four

We sat at the foot of the altar, each absorbed in our own thoughts. I found it difficult to accept the confusion of life, death, pain, and even happiness that is awarded to each of us.

We looked at each other at the same moment.

"I envision why the Master chose you for his apprentice. You have a strong spirit," replied Laotzu.

He reached for the talisman around my neck. He gazed at it for a long time.

"You are wearing a symbol of the four around your neck."

"Yes," I said. "It is a gift from Aryia, daughter of the master merchant Chinsha. It means a great deal to me because it was a special gift but I do not know what it means."

The Priest dropped the amulet and it fell back on my neck. He began to explain the significance of the four. "This Talisman is a gift of friendship and love to the possessor. There are four ways to react to another human being in this life. All are choices, all significant."

I was confused but listened intently.

The priest held up one finger and explained. "One: To recognize someone—anyone—but look away as if they do not exist or matter. Deep in the soul of every person, even though they might not be aware of it, is a knife to the soul. It does not matter why, as this is the most basic of relationships and what people do to keep from getting involved with one another. We are all connected to each other like a spider's web, and the relationship of one is the least amount of connection you can give."

He raised two fingers and said, "Two: Acknowledge an acquaintance with a hello and friendly smile. This is for someone you may like but do not know. You can look into their eyes with love or hate."

Then three fingers. "Three: Acknowledgment of a closer relationship, somewhat like two, however, you might also touch them in a familiar manner, be it on the shoulder or a handshake. This is for closer acquaintances or those that you want to test your relationship with. It is reserved for those you feel can be approached."

Then he held up four, looking just like the symbol on the necklace. "Four: This is the closest relationship. It is a connection of total trust. This is for those closest to you, with a strong and loving embrace or a kiss to those you love or for those you trust and feel a deep kinship."

"Those who live with the philosophy of the four have a loving embrace in their hearts for all humankind. It is a simple way of life, but has a great message about how we react as individuals toward one another."

As the priest continued talking, I watched him closely. "I do my best to live my life with an embrace for everyone in my heart." He smiled at me and I felt he meant it. "You will be given shelter to recover from your physical pain. Take as much time as you need to heal. I will be here when you are ready to learn of the Great Spirit."

It took me some time to heal and regain my full strength, but eventually all my energy returned and I was even stronger. In the temple they had a different way of living. There were few people, all there either to maintain the holy place or finding peace and comfort. Great humility was felt with a sense of love and light.

My Question

For a time I pondered my questions about the Great Spirit and what it meant to me. Soon I asked to meet with Laotzu as I was ready with my first question.

I was led to a beautiful garden full of trees, green plants, purple roses, and sweet alyssum of the most brilliant pinks, purples, and even different colors of white. Laotzu sat under a tree in deep meditation.

He looked up when he heard me approaching.

"Young Shinhon! It is good to see you and the way your body has healed." He motioned for me to sit down. "How has your stay at the temple been so far?"

"Very well, and the temple is a peaceful place; so much so that all cares seem to fall away. Everything is good and there seems to be no evil, at least that is the way I feel."

"Yes, everything is here to cultivate a connection with the Great Spirit," the Priest remarked.

"I have a question, Master Laotzu," I asked. "If the Great Spirit is real then why doesn't he stop malicious things from happening to us?"

He did not answer at first.

Once more Laotzu spoke, "I want you to go see two people and when you return tell me what you have learned of this question and let me know if you have an answer."

I looked at the priest wondering if maybe he was the Master in disguise. No, Laotzu was a follower of the Master, and I was sent to him for his knowledge.

Laotzu gazed into one of the beautiful pink flowers, and I didn't know if he was meditating or thinking about what to say next. I said nothing, but sat there, taking in the scenery. Then he spoke. "You will first go to the largest house in the village to the north. There dwells the village leader, a kind man named Mibil. Listen carefully to this man. After you have spoken with Mibil you will go see another. At the end of the village, on the east side, lives a man named Peebal. You will call on him also and talk with him. As you talk with these men I am sure the answer to your question will be satisfied."

Struggle to Be Great

I went to see Mibil that day. I couldn't help but be excited to hear his point of view.

I took in the beauty of this simple and beautiful village, nestled beneath the great mountains. The home of Mibil was huge, but I did not think it was extravagant. I knocked on the door and a young man opened it.

"Yes what can I do for you?" he asked.

"I am looking for Mibil the leader of the village. I am Shinhon and came from the temple at the request of Laotzu, the priest."

"Oh yes, come in, Shinhon. We have heard that you were here. I also heard of the honor you earned. I thought of you as an older man. Mibil is my father. I will get him for you. He will be delighted you are here."

In a few minutes a man with bright eyes appeared before me. The light of happiness surrounded him.

"Hello friend, Shinhon. My name is Mibil. Has your stay in the temple been satisfying for you? I understand that your journey across the desert was not a pleasant experience." I nodded my head and said, "It was a terrible experience; one that I thought would surely take my life."

"I understand that the Master has an important mission for you here?" he said.

I told Mibil that Laotzu had asked me to come and visit him and I asked that he tell me about his life and how he became leader of the village."

I spent a great deal of time with Mibil as he told me his story. He told me that he loved life but it was not always easy for him. He grew up on a run-down farm with only him and his mother to care for it. His father died when he was a small child and the farm grew fallow. It was a hard life and he had to grow up fast.

He stated that at times he complained and wondered why life had to be so difficult and why they didn't have enough to eat. One day, in despair, his mother asked him to take their only cow to the market to sell for whatever he could get. He explained that he was young and gullible. As he walked to the market he passed a stranger on the road who asked what he was doing. He explained to the stranger that he was on his way to the market to sell this cow.

The stranger told Mibil that he had something that was much more valuable than a cow. He told him that he could see in Mibil's heart and eyes that he was a special boy and that the mysterious man might be willing to make a trade.

"What do you have to trade?" Mibil asked him?

The stranger reached in his pouch and pulled out what he said were magic beans. Mibil got excited and thought of surprising his mother with magic beans. The stranger told Mibil the beans were rare and hard to find, but he was one of the lucky ones who possessed them and got them from a faraway place. There was something about this man that sparked of magic.

He handed Mibil the pouch that was made of beautiful brown leather. The strange man said, "I will make the trade with you since you seem like an honest boy."

Mibil gave him the cow in return for the beans. He was mystified at the thought of magic beans and how they could change their lives. Mibil knew his mother would be happy and that he had been wise to trade their old cow for magic beans! Funny, he did not ask what was magic about the beans. But he was still a young man, excited about life and the idea of magic.

His mother was very surprised to see him home so soon. He could not wait to share the magical beans with her.

"Why are you home so soon," she asked? "How did you sell the cow at the market so quickly?"

He told her the story of the man and the magic beans, proud of his good trade. He was surprised to see that she was not happy. In fact, she looked disappointed and defeated. She sat down on her cot and cried.

After a moment she stood up and threw the bag of beans out of the window. "I don't know what we will do to survive now, Mibil." She cried placing her delicate hands on her face and told Mibil to leave the room. "Go, Mibil, I do not want to look at you right now. I thought I had taught you better than to let someone swindle you out of our last resources."

Mibil didn't know what to say to his dear mother. Instead of making her happy, He seemed to have made it worse for her. He went to bed in anguish.

He did not sleep well, waking up and going back to sleep. He did not want to remember his mother's face and sleeping made the disappointment in him fade. Then he had a dream.

The dream started with Mibil awaking in the morning to find that the beans had grown to one giant bean stock. It was so massive that it had grown into the clouds. How amazing, he thought in the dream. He decided to climb this massive structure to see how far it really grew.

He came upon a land far up in the clouds. Dreams can be so funny. On the island in the sky there was a castle. It was gigantic. He was just a tiny little person compared to this massive place. So small, in fact, that he could crawl under the door.

As he went into the castle he found a giant of a man. As he watched he saw that the giant had a beautiful stark white goose. Mibil stood in awe as this giant asked the goose to lay for him and immediately the goose delivered a golden egg. It was solid gold. Amazing, he thought in the dream. If he had that goose, all he and his mother's problems would be over. Mibil waited until the giant fell asleep, then stole the goose.

The giant awoke to see the goose was gone and ran to catch the boy. Mibil was able to get down the bean stalk fast with his prize and chop it down before the giant got to him.

Mibil awoke that morning excited to look out the window and see a giant bean stalk, but there was only a bag of beans right where his mother had thrown them.

He decided to take the beans and plant them. Not much would grow in the dirt on their farm but he planted all that was in the bag.

It was difficult during those times as they had nothing. Still, his beans began to grow very well. They were big and strong. Not big enough to grow into the sky but they were magic because they did grow hardy in the foul soil.

He worked the farm hard, at times thinking he would die from exhaustion. But that year they had a large crop of beans. They were able to sell them at market and they had plenty to eat.

It was not easy but the poor family survived. The next year they grew an even bigger crop of beans and the year after even bigger. Mibil grew up and became a great bean farmer. He married well and had a large family—seven children who lived on small farms surrounding the city. As they grew up they took care of all the work on the farms. They worked hard because Mibil felt it important for his children to learn through the stress of the farm life.

Mibil became well respected and was eventually asked to be the leader of the village. They always had an overabundance of beans, and no one in the village ever went hungry. If they did not have money to pay, they helped out on the farm. It all worked out well.

He had finished his story and I couldn't stop staring at this man; a person grown strong from hardship and belief in the nature of this world. The Great Spirit was inside him, so much so that he glowed.

"I tell you this, Master Shinhon, I am grateful for the hardships in my life. If I had no adversities and everything was just given to me, I would not have grown the way I did. Hardships give us opportunity to stretch and grow, a chance to become bigger than we were before. I am the man I am today because I chose to grow larger than my problems. We can choose to shrink and let our difficulties drown or suffocate us or we can grow, learn, and find solutions, thus becoming stronger than our troubles. Adversity has made me a better man. I am grateful for the man I am now because of what I learned from the hardships I have had."

Easy Life Makes a Hard Life

I thought of what Mibil had said but wondered if he really knew that his life was better because it was harder. So what if he had an easy life? What if he had been given everything? Couldn't he have been a good person even if he had not lost his father or had to work so hard to stay alive? I could not understand why we had to go through hardships to become better.

For an instant, I did think of the First Wisdom and how much stronger one becomes with physical stress, but are hardships in life the same?

After thanking Mibil for his time I asked where I could find the wise man, Peebal. Mibil laughed, gave me directions, and said, "Good luck."

I was directed to a run-down house at the end of the village. I couldn't believe that anyone of stature would live in such squalor. I knocked on the door.

A large fat man came to the door. "Hello," he said. "Who are you and what do you want. I am a poor man and have nothing to offer you."

I felt uneasy as I said, "My name is Shinhon. The priest, Laotzu, sent me to you."

He then bid me to come in and offered me a rickety chair to sit in. The man could barely walk carrying his massive flab. He sat on a ragged pillow in the middle of the floor. He offered me a cup of something. I refused because the cup was so stained and looked dirty.

"Why are you here?" the obese man asked.

"I have come to talk of your life and learn from you," I replied.

The man told me his story.

He said it was a sad story that he must tell. Peebal was born of goodly parents who loved and cared for him. One night when he was a young child Peebal had a terrible dream, awoke very frightened, and told his parents what he had dreamed.

Peebal was playing atop a great wall. He was big and round and in the shape of an egg, with skinny arms and legs. He was playing on the wall and fell. As he fell he cracked open into many pieces. His parents were there and did all they could to put him back together, bandaging his entire cracked body. No matter how hard they tried they could not put him together again. An army arrived on horses and they also said there was nothing they could do for him. Peebal awoke crying and he told his parents of the dream. When he told his parents, they feared this dream was an omen and said that as long as they lived, they would make sure Peebal was protected.

They did everything possible to keep him safe. He was not allowed to play with others or work in the field as they did. He was given everything he wanted. He never found a wife but depended entirely on his parents. Peebal's parents both grew old and died. Peebal was sure he would die as well, but the village had mercy on him. They gave him enough to survive. Poor Peebal had lived a sad life. In reality, he wished he had fallen off a wall and died. Peebal explained to me that he was only waiting to die.

I felt sorry for him and so did everyone else.

It was hard to be with him due to his deep melancholy. I asked him if there was anything I could do for him. He asked me to fix him a meal because he was not good at cooking. I felt pity for him and fixed him a good meal with the meager provisions he possessed.

He had two small eggs and, as I looked at the eggs, I thought of his dream and something came to me in a strong vision. I was enlightened by the message his dream was supposed to give him. I put wood in the stove and boiled an egg. Peebal stared as I said, "I have two eggs in my hand."

"Yes I see."

I dropped them both on the floor.

The hard-boiled egg just bounced around on the floor, damaged only with small cracks, but the raw one splattered in a mess of egg mingled with shell.

I told Peebal the difference between the hard-boiled egg and the one that was not yet cooked is that you must take much better care of the raw egg then the boiled one. When the egg is boiled it becomes much stronger. "The dream was a warning that your parents missed. They failed to acknowledge the warning and you paid the price. Your parents should have let you play and get scratches and cracks like all other children. Your parents had good intentions, but instead of protecting you, they carried you around on a soft pillow and you have become without substance, soft and raw inside. The boiling water of life is always there to strengthen and teach us."

I asked Peebal if he knew the leader of the town, Mr. Mibil. He said he did and Mibil was a great man. I told Peebal of Mr. Mibil's hardships and the dream Mibil had that assisted him in becoming the great man that he was.

Mr. Peebal looked sad, and stared at his fingers as they curled upward.

I continued speaking, "Now the town is doing the same as your parents. They are now keeping you soft by taking care of you. They are the army that could not put you together. Mr. Peebal, if you do not want the life you have now then change it by doing something different. You are still alive, and while you still live, there is always time for change; you can make choices that can and will make you happier."

"What can I do? I know nothing and am too weak and fat to do anything," the poor sad man said.

"If that is the only thing you believe, then that is what you will always be. Ask the Great Spirit for help in guiding you to your new life."

I told the man, Peebal, of the wisdoms I had learned from the Master. I also told him about the physical and how we grow through learning or we die inside. We may be alive on the outside, but are rotting from the inside. Here is a suggestion: Offer your services to work for a farm in this area. It will be difficult at first and you may feel like you will die because your body has known nothing but sloth. I guarantee you; you will become stronger and sturdier. Of course you will make mistakes but trust yourself and believe you will learn and you will have a better life, certainly better than you do now.

There was a glimmer of understanding in his eyes.

Then I told him I must go. I also said not to let anyone cook his meals any more and to find a simple job to do. Your life is only over if you allow it to be, or if you change your attitude toward yourself. You must also love yourself.

It is a truth that as we struggle with life we get more out of it. If we have everything, we appreciate nothing. We see hardships in life as bad or sad for us, or we can choose to learn and see a better outlook on life.

I told the sad man, "I thank you for teaching me. I only ask that you please consider what I have said and do something different. Only you can change your life with the choices you make. As you struggle in life and fight to do more, you will become stronger and learn to love life."

"Thank you Master Shinhon." He looked up at me with tears in his eyes. "I will always remember your wisdom and I will do more to change my life."

I told Peebal I was grateful to him for allowing me to visit and share his life story with me. I wished him a good life and left for the temple. I had a better understanding of why life had hardships and discovered that I could choose to see them as bad or good. Things that did not kill made you stronger.

I left the rundown house with a greater understanding of why hardship in life assist us in growth. The Great Spirit answers for good or bad without emotion. Attitude is everything. The Great Spirit will guide us, but not protect us, from the hardships in life that assist us in growing.

In that moment I understood the growth that comes from hardship. I thought about those who had nothing to do and let others do everything for them. Did they learn about life? What did they think about? Without any hardships, how would they know the joys of life? I could now see that a loving Great Spirit would want us to flourish, otherwise why would we be here? How could we learn? Hardships are for our own good. I thought of the poor man, Peebal, who was given everything and was never able to learn for himself.

I thought of my family as I reflected on both men and the new lessons I had learned from each of them. Even though I was beginning to comprehend, I was still very sad at the thought of my family being murdered in such a senseless manner. My thoughts turned to my younger sister and brother. They would never have a chance to learn about anything other than our village. Anger zapped through me as I thought of the warlord. I still felt hatred in my heart but, now, the thought of killing him seemed a blameless idea. In one instant, I went from happy to hateful. The feelings were so different: one made me feel light and the other heavy with hatred. I still found it difficult to comprehend how the death of a loved one could assist us in growing and how the ones that died no longer had a chance to learn and grow.

I went back to the temple and asked to see the priest. He was again at the altar in deep meditation. I sat beside him. "Were your visits with Mibil and Peebal helpful in answering your question?" he asked.

I explained to Laotzu that it was enlightening. I do see how hardships in life assist us in growth if we choose to allow it, or if we choose the other side, it can make us helpless, hopeless, and feeling sorry for ourselves.

With a questioning look, I said, "I do have a hard time understanding how the Great Spirit can allow anyone to murder small children like my brother and sister. They cannot learn any more from this life. Their life was taken from them by an evil man." A flash of hatred showed on my countenance.

"Yes," the priest said. "Again, the Great Spirit lets others learn their own lessons in life. The ones who murdered your family needed to have the opportunity to learn. The choice each of us makes in life is for some kind of growth. If the Great Spirit stopped progression people could not grow due to the consequences of their own decisions. For example, you have become a different person because of the deaths of your family.

"So many emphasize the sadness of death, but death is only another part of life. Your family now is in another world learning new things."

"Someone else told me that," I said, thinking of General Yosha.

Laotzu replied, "Those who die will continue to learn, even as spirits. Do not fear for them and release the hatred that is in your heart. It hurts no one but you. Hanging on to hatred and anger is like drinking poison. Let it go."

I was hoping I could let it go, as the priest made so much sense, but I could still see the cold eyes of the warlord and rage boiled inside me. I concentrated on the wisdom of Laotzu.

Doubt

"There are no accidents in this life, young Shinhon. Everything is for a reason. We do not always understand, but there is a reason for everything that happens to us. The Great Spirit is always guiding, yet, everyone is in control of their own destiny with every choice they make."

Thinking, I spoke, "I wish I could talk with the Great Spirit and question him about my doubts."

"You can," the wise priest replied.

"I can?" I said.

"Yes, you can." he said again.

"How?"

"You just have to talk to him. The key is how to listen."

Laotzu looked at me. Putting one hand on my shoulder, he said, "I want you to do something. I would like for you to stay in your room here in the temple. I will have food and water sent to you but I ask that you do nothing but talk to the Great Spirit. Speak with the Great Spirit in silence and you will feel meaning in your heart. When you are done, come and tell me of your experience."

I did as I was asked and sat in my room alone. I talked and felt that I was talking to myself. Hours went by and food was brought to me but I did not eat. I was consumed with a desire for an answer to my questions. I yelled in anger and cried in deep despair, then laughed at the stupidity of talking to myself. I lost track of time and space.

I yelled, "I am done. You are not there. There is no Great Spirit. You are conjured up in our minds to make us feel better about the adversities in life. If you were real, you would let me know."

I was on my knees on the floor with my hands clasped together.

I said again, "If you were real you would let me know." The only thing that could describe what happened is that a bolt of lightning from the room entered my body. Every muscle locked in place and I fell to the floor.

With tears in my eyes, I said. "If you were real, you would let me know."

Even as I said it I realized that the shock to my body was not from me. I began to comprehend another presence.

"You are there?" I said aloud.

In my heart and soul a voice spoke softly and peacefully.

"Yes."

I sat up on the floor of my room, "You are real."

"Yes," the voice came again.

"How do I know that this is not a trick of my mind? I do not know how long I have been in this room."

"You do not know," the soft voice replied. "It could only be in your mind."

"How can I know for sure?" I said.

"It is up to you. I have given you what I can but it is up to you whether you believe or not."

"I doubt." My voice was soft and subtle.

"Doubt is a strong tool. It is the catalyst that moves the human race to learn more. Shinhon, all physical life was put in this realm to experience another part of existence."

"How do I know what I hear is real?" I pleaded.

"It is up to you. There are four acknowledgments of the spiritual"

"One, you believe in nothing. There is only you and this terrestrial life."

The voice continued, "Two, you believe that there may be a spiritual world but you live your life and feel as though it doesn't matter what you do. You even suppose that I do not care what you do."

"Three, you believe I am here to assist and guide you."

"And four, you know I am here and I touch all of your life."

"It is like the symbol of the four around your neck. One, I am ignored. Two, I am acknowledged but kept at a distance. Three, I am touched as a gentle hand on the shoulder. Four, I am fully embraced. All is perfect for those who choose the gift of knowledge. The experience impresses and teaches what is best in this life. I am unconditional love and, in me, all my spirit children are the same. They are loved by me. I ask that you learn and study about me."

I cried, with tears flowing down my face, "What if this is all a lie that I have conjured up to make me feel better about this world? I feel there is just nothingness after this life."

Then I heard the soft voice again, "What have you lost by having me with you? Whether real or imagined I am always here for you. In this life when you are alone it is always more difficult and this is how some chose to learn. Having me with you in your heart is comfort and love. As you focus outside of your life you will see a much fuller and majestic world. Those who focus only on themselves learn a different lesson. Be outwardly focused and look to me and you will ripple through the world with an upsurge of goodness and light. This happens whether I am real or not. It is a law of the universe. There is no argument that there is energy throughout the cosmos that must obey the laws of existence. Focus outside yourself and the powers of the universe will be given you. There are many spirits throughout the world that assist me. Feel them and let them lead you. Learn of me."

I awoke from the floor not knowing how long I had been asleep. I stood in my room and asked, "Are you there?"

I heard a soft voice behind all the garbage of thought possessing my mind. My heart felt warm and peaceful.

"Yes, always," it said.

I left my room a different person. I had talked with the Great Spirit and lived through all my emotions. The Great Spirit did indeed talk back. Before this experience it seemed I had been alone, but now I could feel the many spirits there to assist me on my journey.

Then, I went to see Laotzu.

The priest looked at me. "You are a changed man, Shinhon. I can see it in your countenance. You have been enlightened with true Wisdom of the Spirit. Know that as you take time to talk to the Great Spirit every day the connection you feel will never be broken."

"I did connect and was told to learn of him, so, I ask you, Laotzu: How can I now learn of the Great Spirit and all matters of the spiritual?"

"Come with me," the priest said.

He led me down to a place in the temple that I had not yet seen. We entered a massive room. There were people all around and scrolls everywhere.

Laotzu spoke again, "This is the great library of the temple. There has been much written about the Great Spirit as you can see. This is where you will learn everything there is to learn about all spiritual things and how the world connects with all the powers of the other side. There are many different languages and many different writings by holy people."

"I cannot read," I said.

He answered saying, "You have learned the Wisdom of Learning haven't you?"

"Yes," was my reply, "Until now I believed it was the most important and could not see that there could be any other."

The Priest's response was, "Learning is the meaning of life, what you learn is as important as how much you digest. You learn to know what works or doesn't work for you."

Laotzu pointed his finger over the great room and said, "You can stay here as long as you like. You can be taught to read the ancient scrolls and learn what you will of the spirit. Spirit is not just the Great Spirit. He is the captain of the ship of existence, but there are still things to learn about the sea."

I lost time as I studied in the temple for what must have been years. Throughout those days I lived and talked with Laotzu. I added daily prayer along with the warrior training that Makato had taught me. Makato knew of the First Wisdom and had explained to me that exercising every day would keep my body in good physical form. The warrior's exercises were simple and strong exertion on the body. I also ran through the mountains daily. The temple had simple food and my body and mind stayed strong. I often ran to the top of the mountain where the temple stood. There I seemed to be overlooking the whole world and I talked with the Great Spirit.

Spirit

After a few years it was time to go back to the Master. I knew now that I was connected to this wisdom. I explained to Laotzu that it was time for me to go and he agreed.

He said, "It has been an honor to have your presence in the temple. I bless you to always be open to the spirit. I will give you an embrace that symbolizes the four of relationships. He wrapped his arms around me for a moment and continued speaking, "There is a caravan leaving to cross the desert in a few days. I suggest you travel with that particular caravan. The leader knows where he is going."

I smiled at his small joke.

"Thank you Master Laotzu. You have been a wise and splendid teacher. The Wisdom of the spirit will always be present in my heart."

I bid my friend and mentor good bye. I meditated for the remainder of my time in the temple. Then, I left with the caravan.

I experienced a difficult journey but nothing like the one to the temple. The desert was hot and cold. I was sad to leave what had been my home for a time, but now that I was on my way I was excited to see the Master again and felt a thirst for the next wisdom.

At last, I stood at the gate of the palace.

"I am here to see the Master." I said in a confident voice.

The guards exclaimed, "You are Shinhon, the one who left on a quest for the Master. You destroyed the evil ones to the north. It has been a long time."

"I have been gone for quite a while but I am here now to talk to the Master. Will he see me?" I asked.

My presence was announced and the Master asked for me. Once again, I stood at the end of the stairs and looked up at the Master.

"It has been a long time since I sent you through the desert to tell the priest that there is no Great Spirit. Did you find the priest?" he asked.

I looked at this great man with confidence and said, "Yes, I did, Master."

I had forgotten his mesmerizing gaze. He looked in my eyes and said with a smile, "Did you tell him there was no Great Spirit?"

"No Master, I did not?" I said.

The Master asked what I had learned of this life wisdom.

"Master, I left on my journey believing you must think highly of me due to your continued support of my ignorance of the spiritual world. I was excited about my travel through the desert but I cursed you as I lay burning in the sun. I had been through much and knew that you were a master teacher, but I still doubted you, even thinking you had sent me to die in the desert."

The Master shook his head, "Doubt is a powerful tool. There have been great doubters throughout the world and many times the world has changed because of doubting. Many doubters discover a new enlightenment. Change happens because of doubts."

"I was told the same thing by the Great Spirit," I said.

With a powerful gaze, the Master spoke again. "You must always question when in doubt. The one who knows he does not have all the answers is the one who has wisdom. As you know now, the one place to get true answers to your questions is through the spiritual forces. You were open to the answers. You needed to find your own answers within the spirit of the universe. When a student is ready, the teacher will arrive. So I ask again, what of this Wisdom have you learned?"

I told the Master, "I walked with the priest many days. In my time at the temple I asked numerous questions and learned many things about the Great Spirit. I know now why life is full of hardships and trials. I may not like it and wish for them to be taken away but, like a loving parent to myself, I must allow myself to find the way.

It must be difficult for the Great Spirit to see us suffering since we cause most of it ourselves. I now know that I am heard and can talk with the Great

Spirit through prayer and meditation. If I listen and am open to the spirit I can hear what is said to me. I learned to read the ancient scriptures about the experiences of others with the spirit. As I studied and learned about spiritual things I got closer to the Source.

"Master, I see now that there are wisdoms beyond just learning. The spirit is about being aware of your soul and connecting with other spirits. As this wisdom is put in front of me I now see that it was always there."

The Master spoke, "you have been a good pupil. I have watched you grow and learn from your tasks. I am proud of you. All mortals are imperfect, but as we see our weaknesses and learn from them, we move that much closer to enlightenment. It is good to see you and know of your closeness with spirit. I want you to stay in the palace for a few days and rest after your journey through the desert. I will call for you and we will start your next wisdom."

The Master looked approvingly and said, "Wisdom is learned and driven by the spirit and mind. Only by comprehending the differences of each, will you find true enlightenment.

WISDOM

"Service which is rendered without joy helps neither the servant nor the served. But all other pleasures and possessions pale into nothingness before service which is rendered in a spirit of joy."

MAHATMA GANDHI

City of Chee

A few days passed and I spent my time meditating in prayer and staying in good shape with my military exercises. I also ran outside of the palace. I felt good and was excited to find that my thirst for learning and love of life had grown. I also knew that not only learning was great but the experience along the path to learning was something to appreciate. I was enjoying the journey.

Soon, a servant knocked on my door and told me the Master requested my presence.

As I stood in front of the Master I began to see him and connect with him. I felt a love and friendship from him and for him.

"Are you ready for your next wisdom?" he asked.

"Yes, I am, Master." I answered.

The Master spoke, "You are to go to the northwest city of Chee and there you will give service to three people. Your goodwill is to change their lives,"

I questioned, "Who are they?"

"I do not know," said the Master.

"How will I know who they are?" I asked.

The Master smiled and answered, "Again, I do not know. As you now know the only way to comprehend the wisdoms of life is to learn for yourself by doing. The Master's face lit up. I will give you plenty of money to live on. You are to return when you have learned this wisdom and explain each service to me and what it taught you."

I was somewhat confused but had learned if you let go of the confusion you will know that, as the journey unfolds, all will come to you. I nodded to the Master and was off for my last night's sleep in the palace.

The next day I was given a bag of gold and enough provisions to make it to the city. It was a good journey through beautiful countryside unlike that of the north lands and the desert to the west.

I made it to the city of Chee, a huge metropolitan area, not as big as Hiin, but large. It was a city of great contrast, as there were many riches and much poverty. It was easy to find lodging when people realized that I was not a vagabond and that I had money. The way people looked at me was different than when I pretended to be a beggar. I stayed in an inn that was quite comfortable with all the amenities of the wealthy.

The market was an extraordinary place, much the same as the market of Hiin, yet somehow more diverse. I was unaware that some of the goods in this market even existed. The merchants would yell at people passing through, asking them to buy their merchandize. Such magnificent things were offered. They had the finest clothing and jewelry. Also, there were foods of every kind. I tried many things but was frugal with my money, knowing that I was in the city of Chee for a purpose, not knowing how long I would be there.

The Crippled Beggar

For a few days I did not find anyone to give service to, but was confident I would find someone I could help. I did notice a crippled man with a mangled foot sitting in one corner of the market. He held up a cup as people went by. A beggar, I thought. The man was a sad sight to look at. He was unclean and I thought to myself that he must be 'touched in the head' as well. People would pass by him without a glance.

I decided that I would give service to this man. I took a gold piece out of my purse and put it in his cup. I knew this man had probably never seen that much money before. He said, "thank you kind sir," and off I went thinking that I might not be here long if service was that easy. I had already assisted one person and had only been in the city for a few days. It felt good helping, but I wondered if this was the right kind of service. The thought kept troubling me.

The next day I went to the market feeling refreshed and ready once again to try some new things. I thought of all my past journeys, and knew that life on this earth could and should be enjoyed.

Again I saw the crippled beggar. He was back in his spot. He had a bad cough and his overall look was sickly. I thought to myself that I had already assisted that man and no longer needed to worry about him. I could hear his cough as I wandered about the market place.

I could no longer ignore him. I walked over to the crippled man, and asked, "Sir, are you okay?"

"I have felt better," the man said. Then, as he coughed violently, he continued, "I am sorry young man but it looks as though I have come down with some illness and could die. I am sure there are much worse things." He laughed while coughing and trying to catch his breath. He was quite cheerful for a poor, dying, crippled man, I thought, despite what I felt yesterday, he seemed to have a witty mind.

"I will assist you back to your home," I said.

The beggar's hoarse voice was barely audible as he said, "I do think it would be better than dying here in the market square. Thank you. My name is Mitsuo."

I looked at the sad fragile man and as I let him wrap his weak arm around my shoulder I said, "My name is Shinhon."

I carried him as he directed me to a run-down part of the city.

Soon we arrived at a door. "This is my home," he exclaimed. I opened the door to a tiny room with a small dilapidated stove in one corner. There was a simple cot on the floor. I assisted him to the bed. The cough was getting worse. He was hot and flushed. I filled his small wooden bucket with water from a well at the end of the street.

After he finished drinking a large glass of water, I put a cold cloth on his forehead. He slept fitfully but settled a bit during the night. At times I wondered if he was dead. I stayed with him for many days and soon his health began to improve. Mitsuo was a pleasant man to talk to and had a good attitude, even with the shortcomings he had experienced in life.

He told me that he would need to get back to the market soon because the landlord would want the rent and he would also need money for food. He coughed loud and hard, which seemed to make him feel a little better. I told him that for now he should not worry. I would take care of all his needs.

At first Mitsuo was leery of my kindness. I would catch him looking out of the corner of his eye in wonderment and disbelief.

I told him of the Master and that I was here to do service as one of my lessons in the wisdoms of life. "Again, my name is Shinhon. Have you heard of me as the one who assisted the Great General Yosha in the city of Tal?"

The old crippled man looked at me, "The land you speak of is far away and we do not hear much news from the north. I have not heard of you, but I thank you for your kindness."

After many days he felt at ease with me. He said that there must be something he could do to repay me for my kindness. I told him that he owed me nothing for my service.

One morning I was awakened by Mitsuo cooking something at the stove. "Good morning," he exclaimed. "I have decided to cook you some of my mother's special cake. It is a family recipe that my mother taught me. As a young boy I was sickly and could not play with the other kids so I watched my mother cook and learned everything about the art of baking from her."

Mitsuo was meticulous as he blended different ingredients. As he made the cakes on the stove the aroma was astonishing. I do not believe I have ever smelled anything as sweet and tantalizing as those cakes. He had mixed nutmeg with cinnamon and other ingredients, creating an incredible fragrance when blended together. They also looked perfect.

"I don't usually splurge like this but you have done so much for me," he explained.

He took the cakes off the stove and set them aside to cool. I did feel quite hungry and the aroma made me even hungrier.

"Here you are young master Shinhon," Mitsuo said.

As I bit into the cake I couldn't believe how delicious it tasted as it melted in my mouth. It was by far the best cake I had ever eaten. Compared to the Master's pastries in the palace this cake was much superior.

After the wonderful breakfast I told the man I would go to the market and get whatever he needed in the way of supplies. He asked for some simple things and off I went to the market.

Even though I had lots of experience with vending while staying with Chinsha, I was still amazed at the market. There were many food items to choose from: spices, flour, milk, and many other ingredients. But the taste of that wonderful cake would not leave my head or nostrils. I found a merchant selling pastries. I bought the best-looking sweetbread I could find. It was good, but nothing compared to Mitsuo's cake. As I stood in the market eating the not-so-good pastry, I looked around and thought how many people in the market would love Mitsuo's cake just as much as I had.

My heart began to race as I thought about the business this man could generate with the cakes. I began to realize that real service is teaching those who are down-trodden. This was so much better than giving something that would only last a day. I was thrilled that I could be of service to this man and possibly change his life. Could there be any better service than to assist him in becoming self-sufficient?

Amazing Cakes

I bought the provisions and ran to Mitsuo's home. I explained to him that he could make much more money selling his cakes at the market than he could ever get begging for a living. I told him about my experience working with a great merchant in the city of Hiin and that I could assist him in selling his cakes.

He said he could only make two or three cakes on his tiny stove and the ingredients were much too expensive.

I told him that I had come to this city to give service and that I would locate a new place to live with a big stove where he could bake larger quantities. He exclaimed that he could never make enough by himself to sell many and earn a good living. I told him I would assist him.

The next day we went to look for a suitable place with a large stove. We found a home, far from the ghetto where he lived, and it was close to the market. Not only did it have a nice stove but an actual bed to sleep on, with chairs, tables and lamps. It was expensive but I knew it was the perfect place. I paid for the house and we moved his simple belongings to his shiny new home.

Once again I went to the market to get the supplies we would need. The ingredients were expensive and I had spent most of my money setting Mitsuo up in business.

I awoke early after a good night's sleep. Mitsuo was already at the stove, carefully measuring the ingredients like an artist. Soon delicious aromas permeated the room and the samples I ate proved his amazing cake was just as good now as it had been the first time.

I was excited to get the cakes to the market. I knew they would sell. It was as though someone had handed me a pot full of gold; I was exhilarated.

I found some old crates to put all the cakes on and placed a simple lace cloth over the top. We had made many dozens of the small cakes and were ready to take them to the market.

I was only able to carry one crate at a time. Mitsuo helped as best he could. I said we should sell all the cakes in the first few crates and I would come back for more, if needed.

We arrived at the market square early and it was already full of merchants and vendors selling their wares. I thought to myself that we might have to set up earlier to get a head start. The merchants had established locations; some for many years. But luckily so did Mitsuo—his spot in the small corner where he had sat for so many years, begging for whatever anyone would give to him. It was a small spot but out in the open where everyone could see him and suitable enough to sell our pastry. The merchants looked at us as if we were some kind of criminals. We arranged the crates in a V-position so they would be attractive and noticeable. Then, I found a piece of charcoal from a fire and wrote the price and the words, "Delicious and Mouthwatering Cakes for Sale by Mitsuo, the Baker." I placed the sign on the side of the makeshift table.

The day started to get busy. Some people looked at us, most just laughed and went on their way; some even asked where Mitsuo's cup for begging was because he would be sure to get more money begging than trying to sell a cake.

I looked at our sign and wrote above the cakes, "Amazing." So now we have, "Amazing Delicious Mouthwatering Cakes" for sale.

After what seemed like many hours, a woman walked up to us with compassion in her eyes and purchased a cake. She said, "You have my attention and I must try some of your "Amazing Cakes." As she bit into the cake you could see her face light up with the magic I had experienced the first time I tasted Mitsuo's cake.

"This is an amazing cake," she exclaimed. "Could I purchase two more, please?"

A man walking by saw the woman's reaction and, out of curiosity, decided he would try one. He was quite a big man and you could tell that he was a lover of food. His reaction was even more enthusiastic then the woman's. "I will take a dozen of these delightful cakes. I have never tasted such an incredible piece of dessert and I have eaten many pastries in my lifetime," he laughed.

The word spread soon and we were out of cakes. We had sold everything in half a day. We made double the money that we paid for the ingredients. We made as much money as it would have taken Mitsuo to earn in a year.

He was a happy man and so was I. There was great joy in my heart. Doing true service for Mitsuo gave me a warm feeling that I had never felt before. Serving for the general was worthy and receiving prayers from others was also good, but assisting this man, who had nothing and expected nothing in return, gave me a much different feeling. I felt love in my heart that cannot be expressed and obtained a deeper understanding of my fellow human beings.

Lost and Alone

Several days passed and word spread about the amazing pastries of Mitsuo. He was touted as "Mitsuo, the Amazing Baker" and admired for his skills. We worked hard and Mitsuo had a new light and life about him. He loved baking the cakes.

One day as I was walking in the market I saw a merchant holding a young boy. He looked angry. He gripped the boy tight enough to hurt him. I was not sure what came over me but I felt prompted to intervene.

"What is going on," I asked the merchant?

"This little thief was stealing my fruits. I shall have his hands cut off," he said. I looked at the child, not much younger than I was when I started on my quest for the Master. He was defiant but I saw great fear in his eyes.

"What did he take," I asked. "Two pieces of fruit," said the merchant looking down at the boy with disdain. I looked at the boy as well and told the merchant that I would pay for what he had taken. I took the boy by the arm and said, "Give the boy to me and I will see that he is punished."

He was reluctant but having been paid for his goods had calmed him. He glared at the boy as though he hated him. We left the merchant in a hurry.

"Where are your parents?" I asked the young boy.

"They are dead, sir. I have lived on the streets for some time," he announced with strong resilience.

I felt deep pain in my heart as I also knew what it was like to be without parents.

"You have no one?" I asked.

"I was an only child. My parents died from a sickness that swept through the city two years ago. My grandparents were sent to a leper colony to the north of the city when they contracted the disease. I received word that my grandfather had died, but my grandmother was still alive. I was told where they were but that I could not see them. My grandparents and I were close." A tear made its way down his cheek. He wiped it quickly so I wouldn't see it.

The boy's spirit was low. I recognized the look of despair in his eyes. "I need your help," I said to the boy. "My help? I thought you were going to punish me," he replied.

"I only told the man that to make him less reluctant to give you to me." I explained to him that I was here to give service to those who were revealed to me. I felt that he was the one I was supposed to assist. He looked confused.

"What is your name?" I asked him. He hesitated to tell me.

"Uery," he said quietly.

I smiled at him. "Your name means Joy and Strength." He shrugged his shoulders at the irony.

I asked him to follow me back to the baker.

I explained to Mitsuo that I could not assist him much longer and that this young boy, Uery, was willing to aid him for room and board plus a small salary.

Mitsuo had a good heart and I knew he would be glad to take care of the boy. He was grateful that he could be of service to someone and that they would have a shared relationship. He was grateful for his new young worker who appeared to be strong. It was amazing how the demands for his cakes had grown so quickly.

Uery was a hard worker and was happy to have the work to keep his mind on. After many days I could see a great bond grow between the two. It was a love much like father and son. The two of them were compatible and looked like they belonged together; happily working side by side.

One night Mitsuo told me about his dream of being a father and a husband, but he felt with his deformity that this would never happen. No one would want him as a husband. He told me this was a source of remorse in his life.

Soon, we outgrew the new home and had to move to a bigger place.

The money was not a problem so we bought a bigger home. The house was huge, and contained three stoves in a spacious kitchen.

I have happy memories of sitting and talking with both the boy and the baker. The service I had given the two did remarkable things to my heart. I never thought that I could feel love again. I was afraid that my feelings would disappear into a toughness. We experienced laughter and happiness. I could enjoy life again because of service given without expectations of getting anything back.

I Built the Bridge
for You

One night, as we were deep in conversation, Uery spoke of his parent's death and his expression showed great sadness. "I wish I knew what became of my grandmother. She and my grandfather were sent to a leper village and soon after there was word that my grandfather had died of the disease. My grandmother was the kindest and most loving person I had ever known. I only wish she could be aware of my love for her now."

We spoke of his grandmother at length and I could only imagine how she must be worried about him. I asked if he knew where the leper village was located. He said that it was someplace north of the city. I suggested that maybe we should go there and try to find her. I felt an urgent need to let Uery's grandmother know about him. I also thought that maybe she was the third person that I could do service for.

"It is dangerous to go to the village and only few are allowed to trade and send messages to anyone in that terrible place. They do not stay long and they will not let boys of my age go in for any reason," Uery replied with a look of defeat in his expression.

I looked into the sad eyes of the boy and told him I would go see her myself. I will tell her of your whereabouts and what you are doing.

His eyes sparkled as he said, "I would really love to hear from my grandmother. That would make us both so happy, Shinhon. I would be grateful if you would do that for us."

The next day, making sure all was well; I started my journey to the leper village. It was a full day's run from the city but I took provisions to get there and back not wanting to risk disease by using anything from the village.

It was a pleasant journey and while traveling I came upon a massive ravine. It was steep and I knew I could not climb down. The path led away and I could not see how far down it was.

I noticed an old man working on a bridge across the gully.

"Hello," I said.

"Hello young man and a very nice day to you. Are you going north?" he replied.

"Yes, thank you! I am going to the leper village."

The stranger said, "Oh, I see, this bridge will shorten your trip immensely."

I asked him if he made many trips and if he built this bridge because he was tired of going the long way?

He looked at me with a smile and said, "Oh no, I live further to the southeast. This was a one-time trip for me and I am sure I will never be back this way again."

I asked, "Then why did you build this bridge?

"Why not?" replied the old man.

I asked him if building bridges was his work and who he built this bridge for.

"I built it for you," the old man said.

I exclaimed in amazement, "Me, what do you mean?"

"I built the bridge for you, my friend," was his reply.

"How did you know I was coming?" I asked him.

"I knew that you would be coming someday—I saw you in my mind."

Now I was really confused.

Understanding my confusion the old man laughed and told me he knew that someday someone would come and need to use the bridge. "Yes, young man, that someone is you." He winked at me and smiled. His eyes looked soft and knowing like a shaman's eyes.

"You were not asked to build the bridge but saw me coming some day?" I questioned him.

"No I was not asked to build it, except maybe by the Great Spirit, who speaks to anyone who will listen," was his reply.

I said to him, "I am grateful, sir, that you would build this bridge, but I am still confused as to why. I am a man on a journey to comprehend the wisdoms of life and I find you interesting. I've studied and communed with the Great Spirit, but it appears that the small voice inside does not come as easily to me as it does to you."

The old man explained that at the end of your life you will not think of how much money you acquired but you will think of the special changes you made in other people's lives. What we do for others is what will matter. That is the only thing we take with us at the end of our life. Every day I awake and ask myself what I can do for others. I wonder how I can make a difference. Then, I ask the spirit that lives in me, my highest self, how could I be of service each day?

I shook my head in understanding, as I was learning more and more about giving without expecting anything in return.

Then he spoke, "There was a time in my life that I only thought of myself, as I grew up a sickly and selfish person. Every day, I sat around thinking only of how miserable my life was and feeling sorry for myself. I blamed my unhappy life on everything and everyone. Eventually, I considered taking my life as a way to get out of this horrible existence. The weight of life was too much to bear. I wondered what good I was doing and who would miss me. I also thought that it must be a mistake that I was born in the first place.

"I had no friends and no family that would have anything to do with me or care for me. The day I decided to end it all I heard a knock on my door. It was a holy man from the village where I lived. He asked if I was busy. I told him I was busy and asked what he wanted. I was unkind to him, and thought he just wanted something from me."

I listened to the stranger tell his story and pondered the words he spoke. He appeared to be such a wonderful man and it was hard to believe he could ever have been mean or thoughtless.

He continued, "The holy man told me about an old widow woman who could not keep her home up and needed someone to assist her. He also asked if maybe I would be willing to help by making repairs to her home. The only thing useful I ever did was carpentry because I could do it alone. I had learned, or thought I had learned, that no one liked me so I rejected everyone. I was lonely."

He looked sad, shaking his head, and then continued. "I do not know where the 'holy man' heard about my only skill because no one ever asked me for anything in my miserable life. I told him I would help the lady. I had planned my demise so what did it matter if I put it off for one more day?"

I was fascinated by his story.

"There were a lot of repairs to be done for the old woman and I was surprised at how she lived with her house falling down around her. There was always something else that needed fixing. Most of it was hard work but, after a while, a funny thing happened: I began to forget about my own problems while doing service for this woman. We began to enjoy each other's company. Life lightened and I did not feel sick anymore. Thoughts of taking my life were gone and my soul felt stronger but lighter. The service I had given to this woman changed my life forever. This was the greatest and most important lesson of my life.

"I now know that the holy man must have been told by the Great Spirit of my need to assist someone. From that day onward I have spent my life in service to others. I do all I can to make everyone I come in contact with have a better day, without taking away their own power."

I told him that I too had found that service to others was the best way to live. I had discovered the secret to life is to forget yourself and live for serving others. The interesting thing is how service makes you so much happier than thinking only of yourself. Those who serve are the ones who find true happiness.

The old man had a sparkle in his eye as he said, "There are no accidents in this life. I can see we were supposed to meet, young man."

The old man looked up at the sun and rubbed his neck, then said, "I think of my early life and am so grateful that I was open minded enough to learn this lesson of service. Young man, be wide open to the love of the people around you and the sun will always shine upon your head."

I thanked him and told him he had given me deep insight into life. I bid the happy old man good bye and walked across his beautiful bridge. I waved as I continued on to the leper village.

Lose Yourself in Others

I found the road and knew there would soon be a path from the bridge. This path would make the trip for many to the village much easier. As I walked I pondered the old man's wisdom.

I sat down after a time to rest and eat a bite. I blessed the little bit of food I had. While at the temple I had learned to be grateful to the Great Spirit for the small things in my life and a meal was always a good time to give thanks.

After I ate I decided to pray again. The wisdoms I had learned became a greater part of my life. Every day I made it a point to do my warrior exercises to keep my body in tune and to eat good foods close to the earth. I could always tell if I was not physically fit as it affected everything, including my moods and my thoughts.

Prayer was now a part of my life. I loved speaking with the Great Spirit. It was a peaceful time and I was always focused. I was grateful for this wisdom and the peace it gave me.

As I sat and prayed a wonderful calm came over me. I felt the presence of the Great Spirit. Suddenly I was aware of the importance of the wisdom I was learning at this time. The soft voice that I had started to recognize spoke to me.

"As you lose yourself in others your own life will be enriched. How you touch others is a special power that many miss in this life."

As I finished my prayer, knowing the truthfulness of these things, I was happy and went on my way. Late in the day I saw a shepherd sitting on a rock with his faithful dog beside him. I felt so much joy in my heart at the time and was filled with love.

I went up to the shepherd, and said, "Hello, friend shepherd," and with a big smile continued. "What a wonderful day and life this is, don't you agree?"

The shepherd was a little taken aback by my happiness but said, "Yes, I guess it is a good day. All my sheep are accounted for and I have food to eat so, yes, I suppose it is a good day."

"What a fine animal you have beside you," I said. "I can tell he is faithful and good friend."

The shepherd looked at his dog and said, "I must say it would be lonely out here without Shep as he is a loyal friend."

"How lucky you are, friend shepherd," I said.

A smile appeared on his face and he replied with a laugh, "Yes, I suppose I am quite lucky. Being a shepard is a wonderful life and I have learned to love the solitude. I take care of my sheep and protect them and they in turn give me wool to sell at the market. I live under the stars and contemplate the wonders of the world. Shep and I serve each other with loyalty and love."

He offered to share his food with me, but I declined. I bid the shepherd goodbye and continued on my journey. As I walked, I turned back to see the shepherd standing with his friend, Shep, who had his paws on the man's shoulders in a dance of love. They both looked happy. I too felt happy to know that I had played a small but positive part in their lives.

Angel of Service

The journey was not hard. I made it easily to the village. I ran most of the way but stopped to see and feel my surroundings.

I felt a cloud of sadness as I came to the gates. On the outside stood a guard not to protect those inside but to warn away any unsuspecting travelers. I told him I was here to see a woman whose grandson had a message for her. He told me her name was Akia.

The guard said, "I do not know much of what goes on inside the colony, I only let some people from the city come in. I let those in who have charity. You may enter at your own risk." He looked at me with an expression on his face showing great sadness. I thought of all the sorrow that he must see at this gate.

The guard opened the simple gate and I proceeded into the village. Modest huts were spread throughout the area. The stench of death made me feel nauseated. I was startled by the first few people I saw. Most of them had deformities with little of their faces left, and were covered with sores from head to toe. Their hands were shriveled with missing fingers; most of them limped on deformed feet, assisted by a cane or stick.

I asked about a woman called Akia, but no one seemed to know who she was. I found one woman who said she knew her. "She is the angel of the village. I will take you to her."

She took me to a rather large hut, where the stench of death was extreme. The lady who had taken me to this place warned me that this was the most diseased part of the village and that it was also where those who do not have long to live spend their last days. She said the one I call Akia assists them. She is called the Angel of Death, because she cares for and comforts them as they take their last breath.

I walked into the hut and couldn't help but notice the dilapidated cots where sick people lay, moaning with pain. There was such sadness and hopelessness. I saw a woman applying cool water to their hot brows, giving as much comfort as possible. She was the most beautiful woman I had ever seen. Her flowing white hair shone like a candle in this miserable and dreary place. She had no deformities and not one blemish but was perfectly intact. I was captivated by her beauty.

She looked up as I walked over to her and called her by name. The sadness and despair of this depressing place melted away from the face of this woman.

She smiled, "I have not been called that for some time, since my good husband passed away. I am sorry you are here, my son, you are so young to be cursed with this terrible disease, leprosy. I see no signs of the disease on you."

"No," I exclaimed, "I do not have leprosy. I came to give you a message from your grandson."

Her eyes had a twinkle in them, "Uery?" she asked. "I feared him dead. I had only heard recently of my daughter and her husband dying but no one had any news of Uery. I thought he had died along with his parents."

I looked at this beautiful woman, amazed, and said. "Why are you here if you do not have leprosy and how have you kept from getting it all this time?"

She told me her husband had the disease and she followed him to the colony. "I cared for him until he died. He was the love of my life and I could not leave after his death even though I did not have the sickness. I felt I had to stay here and serve others as much as I could. There is so much sadness with this disease. The loss of loved ones is unbearable. My soul has never let me be afflicted by the disease and I know I will be here all my days.

"Is Uery okay, is he happy and well?" she asked.

I told her how I had found him on the streets, but now he worked for the baker and was well cared for.

She began to cry with joy. "Oh, my son, thank you so much. You will never know what it means to me to be aware that my grandson is safe. I wish I could see him but I have been here too long now and they would never let me leave. I don't think I would leave even if I could."

She put her hands on my face, pulling me to her, and gave me a kiss. Looking into her eyes, I could have died in peace, as I knew so many others must have done.

"Tell my grandson how much I love him. A messenger comes once a month to the village. I will write him the next time. Uery is such a good boy and I have been so worried about him. Please tell him of the love I have for him and that I think of him every day. Tell him to close his eyes and meditate and feel the love from me to him."

I looked at this humble woman and said, "I will, and thank you, Akia, for the excellent example you have been to me."

"My son, service is the greatest gift we can give to others and you have given me a most precious gift. I thank you with all my heart," she said with tears in her eyes.

She gave me another kiss, excused herself, and apologized, explaining there was much to be done. I left feeling joy in my heart. Thinking of the power of service gave me much happiness even in this place. I left the village knowing I had completed this wisdom. I felt that I was a fortunate man, indeed.

As I walked out of the village I stopped where the guard stood. "Being a guard here must be a difficult job seeing the sick enter and never come out. I thank you," I said, with deepest sincerity.

The guard bowed his head. "I have never been told that before," he said in a soft voice. He looked up with a tear in his eye. "Thank you," he said.

I prepared to go back to the city.

As I traveled, I pondered over the beautiful lady who had given her life in service to others. It was pure selfless magic.

Secret to a Joyful Life

When I arrived at the city the next day I found Mitsuo hard at work in the market. Uery was there and another boy had joined them. They were eager to see me. "Shinhon, Let me tell you what has happened since you left."

Uery talked to me and introduced the other boy. "This is Yer my close companion on the streets. He is a very good friend. He also lost his parents and Mitsuo was so busy that I asked Yer to assist us. Before his parents died they taught Yer writing and mathematics and I know he will be a great business asset."

"Very good." I said. "I have news of your grandmother. She is well and works long hard hours assisting the dying. She misses you and will send messages now that she knows where you are."

Uery gave me a big hug and said, "Thank you so much, master Shinhon. You are a great holy man."

No, I shook my head. "I am merely in service."

Uery was excited as he explained, "We must tell you. You have become quite a hero here."

"What do you mean? I do not understand." I asked.

Uery explained, "The people were asking Mitsuo how he started selling the amazing cakes instead of begging. He told them the story of how you had assisted him when he was sick and almost died. He mentioned your name and there was a man in the crowd who had come from the city of Hiin. The man knew the name, Shinhon."

"The man told everone that you were a great warrior and engineer of magical devices when you were in the north and that you were the Master's disciple, a very spiritual man. Your name had traveled fast through the city and there were others who had heard of you as well."

I didn't know what to say.

"The people are now saying you are the great holy man who can turn beggars into successful merchants. This is an exciting time here for everyone. Thank you, Shinhon, for bringing me to the baker. Mitsuo is a good man and Yer and I will do all we can to assist him," said Uery.

As word spread many came to see me. I explained that I was only an apprentice, here to learn, but they wanted to touch and talk with me.

I stayed with Mitsuo and the two young boys that night and told them I needed to be on my way back to the Master. I felt my job was finished and knew that all would be well with them. I didn't want to bid farewell, as I had grown fond of the three people with whom I had served, and in turn they had served me.

After a long journey I stood once again before the Master. He looked at me approvingly and said, "My friend, Shinhon, what did you learn of this wisdom?"

I thought about his question and answered, "Real service is about knowing what is needed for others but I think some would throw a piece of bread at a beggar thinking they are doing good. Service is a powerful thing and the magic is in doing service with love in your heart. If you feel compassion in your heart for others it will open up the power of service and an understanding of how to serve one another. The only way to have true compassion is to be focused on the needs of others and not expect a reward. I never looked at myself or my problems and only focused on those around me. Focusing gave me protection from the sadness of my life and the misery of others. Overlooking the misery in life, I learned that helping others would take this wrongful and negative emotion away.

"I have never known of a secret that was as powerful as the Wisdom of Service.

"Service to others made me forget the pain in my own heart. Helping a crippled beggar become a successful baker, and giving two young boys a new family, caused a sick and bitter man to be a force of good, and helped a woman of complete compassion stay beautiful in a city of disease and death.

"Master, if I never learn another thing in this life I will be happy with this wisdom and now I know that the secret to a joyful life is loving and doing service for others. I am grateful for this wisdom."

The Master looked at me intensely and spoke, "Shinhon, service is an important wisdom but know this, young apprentice, all of the wisdoms are essential. Each of the Eight Wisdoms is critical as they are all connected. The person that who masters them all is the one with ultimate enlightenment. You have grown so much since that day you walked into the palace as a confused boy. There is still more to learn. Don't be deceived.

His genuine eyes twinkled as he looked at me. I felt the warmth of a loving father.

"I want you to rest and enjoy yourself in the palace for a time. Think about all you have learned and link the wisdoms together, seeing how they connect to each other. Meditate on the joy of each one."

WISDOM 5

"As a single footstep will not make a path
on the earth, so a single thought will not
make a pathway in the mind. To make
a deep physical path, we walk again and
again. To make a deep mental path, we
must think over and over the kind of
thoughts we wish to dominate our lives."

HENRY DAVID THOREAU

The Riddle

I spent many days in the Palace enjoying its pleasures. There were beautiful gardens and the peacefulness of the palace was second only to the temple in the mountains. I thought about all the lessons; as the Master instructed, linking the wisdoms together.

I still focused on eating well and exercising. I meditated every day connecting with the Great Spirit and contemplated all that I had learned up to this point. I was excited to learn everything I could and looked forward to the next wisdom.

The Master called for me and once again I stood in front of him, waiting for his insights. I loved being around him as the light that shown from him made me want to be in his presence.

"Shinhon, are you ready for the next wisdom?" asked the Master.

"Yes Master, I am ready. I have contemplated the wisdoms and learned so much. I now see the importance of the wisdoms in everyone's life."

The Master looked into my eyes and explained that he was going to recite me a riddle and wanted me to ponder it as I considered my quest for this wisdom. Upon my return he wanted my interpretation of the riddle.

He spoke with authority as he said, "This is the riddle. I have placed it on a scroll so you will not forget any part of it. What is always with you—at sad times and mad times, at happy times and joyful times? If you do your best to push away, it will stay longer, no matter what you do or say. If you laugh or cry, it will obey, if you feed it, you will become it. It can assist you in moving mountains or stop you from lifting a grain of sand."

He continued, "Remember what I have said, and read the scroll often, as you progress on your new journey. I am sending you south to the bottom of the Cachy Mountains by the great Momotha River. There lies the city of Ivicas. Ivicas is ruled by three wise men; Shim, Shem, and Shom. I want you to go to see them and they will assist you with this wisdom."

"You will be given enough provisions for your trip and a map to the city. After you learn this wisdom I want you to return. You will know when it is time."

I gathered all my provisions and soon was on my way, excited to see what new and wonderful things I would learn.

I pondered the Master's riddle as I traveled. I had already learned enough to know that life can be seen from many perspectives and in many different ways. As I read the scroll over and over, I contemplated which answer sounded correct to me.

"What is always with you at sad times and mad times, happy times and joyful times?" I knew that my body was with me at all times but what did sad or happy times matter. If the answer is my body, it would be with me until I die. But nevertheless it is with me through all phases of my life, both happy and sad periods.

"If you do your best to push away, it will only stay longer, no matter what you say." I cannot push my body away, so the body cannot be the answer to the riddle.

"If you laugh or cry, it will obey." If I laugh or cry that is all there is; I am sad or happy, but there are neutral times when I really don't feel anything. Maybe emotions is the answer?

"If you feed it you will be it." Yes, if I feed or focus on my emotions they become larger, for better or worse.

"It can assist you in moving mountains or stop you from lifting a grain of sand." My emotions don't really motivate, they are just simply there and can change from glad to sad, whatever is happening at the moment.

I was fascinated by the beauty of the pastures, cows and sheep grazing, and flowers dancing in the wind. It made me feel warm all over. Pure happiness was the emotion I was feeling right at that moment. I thought it was interesting that things can happen in life to change your mindset in an instant. For example, a big animal attacking one of the sheep would change everything.

The Dream of Now

I had a delightful and picturesque trip. The countryside looked like the same terrain as the city of Chee. As I got closer to the city of Ivicas, I camped by the great river, Momotha. It was a massive river that stretched through the middle of the Master's land. The only ones who crossed it were the men who ran the ferry rafts. The river was the reason the lands of the Master were so prosperous. The Momotha is fed by many rivers.

That night I slept well but I did have a dream, a powerful, vibrant dream.

In my dream I stood in front of three massive doors. I opened the first door and could see my family. I could not enter the door. In my dream I could only look through the door at the vision of my family and I felt a devastating loss. I wanted to go through the door and be with them.

I went on to the next door and opened it. In front of me sat an old man in a chair. He looked familiar. As I looked closer I could tell it was me as an old man. I thought how nice it would be to talk to myself, ask about everything I had learned in this life, and see if I could find mistakes I had made. But again, I could only see him. I could not walk through the door. I turned to the last door and opened it. There was a river. As I walked through the last door, my eyes opened and I was awake, standing by the river just like in my dream. It was daybreak and as I stood looking at the massive river, I mused over the bizarre dream for some time, knowing that it had to have powerful significance.

I offered my morning prayer, still pondering about the dream and asking the Great Spirit for assistance in understanding it. I finished warrior exercises, packing my belongings, and continued on my way. I was not far from the town and could see Ivicas nestled below the mountains.

Many farms were situated around the village and a cluster of homes surrounded the city square. As I walked to the town I noticed that there was an entrance, not a gate but an arch, and on top of the arch was carved, "Welcome to Ivicas."

I stopped and talked to various people on the street, asking if they knew Shim, Shem, and Shom. The people were friendly and several pointed me in the direction of the wise men. They welcomed me to their village and asked about my travels. A boy pointed to a collection of three houses. He told me those were the homes of the three wise men I was looking for.

I walked toward the houses. In front of the entire group of homes was one great garden; containing shimmering greenery, with plants and remarkable shrubs surrounded by stunning flowers. I thought it must have taken a lot of hard work to keep the garden so beautiful. Each of the three homes was open and inviting; each was distinct and separate. At the entrance of the garden was an arch; and on the arch was carved the words:

"Shim Shem Shom — What you think is what you become." I thought that odd.

I walked through the arch into the magnificent garden. The aroma was delightful. I took the path to the left as it seemed as good as any. I approached the first house on the left. In front of the door was another carving which read;

"The home of Shim — Attitude of the Now"

I knocked on the door and after a time a distinguished looking man answered. He appeared strong but ripe with age. He was thin and looked like a chiseled granite statue. He wore a hat on his head and his long braided hair was running down the length of his back. His robes were sparkling white. I could tell he was a wise man. His eyes twinkled with years of knowledge and wisdom—like the Master's.

"Hello young man, what may I do for you?" he asked.

"My name is Shinhon and I have been sent by the Master to see you and the other wise men."

"It is wonderful to finally see you in person, Master Shinhon. Much has been said about you. My name is Shim. Come in, come in, I am sure you are tired from your journey."

He bid me to enter his home, and then directed me to a warm and cozy room containing soft cloth chairs and a blazing fireplace that kept the entire house warm. The decorations were simple and the walls were sparkling white. The floor looked like chiseled white marble.

Shim pointed to a comfortable looking chair and said, "Please sit, dear Shinhon. Tell me about yourself and what brings you to us."

I started telling him my story, "The Master has sent me on many quests to learn about the wisdoms of life." I told him of my adventures; the good ones and the hardships in my past. As we talked I felt prompted to tell him of the dream I had the night before.

"Oh, that is interesting," he said, "and it is perfect that you came to me." He sat for a while not speaking, as though in deep meditation. Finally he opened his eyes and looked into mine saying, "I can interpret your dream and tell you what I think it means?"

"Yes, I would like that very much," I said.

He started by saying, "As I told you, my name is Shim and I am one of three brothers. I am known as 'The One with the Attitude of the Now.'"

I scooted up closer to his chair.

He leaned toward me and began to speak, "Shinhon, the first door was your past, and as you opened it you saw that you can only view the past, but you cannot change or interact with anything or anyone. You can only see the joy and sadness of what has gone on before. The next door in your dream is your future, and again, you can only see it in the dream, but you cannot interact with it because it has not yet happened. The future is malleable and there are many potential choices in the path you desire to take. "The third door is the present, and is the only door you can walk through, because it is the only plane of existence that you can actually affect."

I nodded my head in agreement.

"Shinhon, many people live their lives in the past, wishing they could have done something different. What they can do is forgive themselves and others, and let go of the past, learning from those experiences and using them to control their life now. Some think only of the future with the attitude that the future is when they will be happy, but, at this time, my life is miserable. No one will ever have a perfect life unless they understand that this erroneous thinking damages both the mind and spirit. The future can be created by meditating on the best possible life now, and trust the Great Spirit to direct choices. They must simply let go, not dwelling on desires, but trust what will take place in their separate lives. The only time we have complete control is now! Dwelling on the past or future only leads to deep despair."

I told Shim that I knew this was true; I had lived through it.

He spoke again, "I have studied the philosophy of living in the now. This attitude has saved my life. When I was a much younger man I was successful in my outer life. I was a young expert in business and had amassed a great fortune. But I began to worry about my life, even though I had experienced much prosperity; I knew something was missing and I worried about future mistakes. There were many who supported me in business. But I was still worried about whether I had made the wrong decisions about all things, and was always worried about the future. At times I found myself dwelling on mistakes of the past, thus punishing myself. All those worries consumed me. I had accumulated so much, but I began to get sick, tormenting myself. My emotions were killing me. It got to the point where I became ill and was told that I did not have long to live. I could only drink sweet tea and eat a special gruel for sustenance."

Shim looked upward continuing his story.

"The moment I was told that death was inevitable, something happened inside me. I thought I was too young and there was still so much for me to do. A transformation came over me and I realized if I did not change my attitude and quit worrying I would miss out on so much in life. All of the worries of the past and future faded away. I got my affairs in order and gave most of my riches to the people who worked for me. I decided if these were my last days I would travel. I wanted to live life to the fullest. Physicians told me I would die faster if I did not stay in bed and rest. The thought of death, just lying in bed, was not what I would choose.

"It had always been my desire to see other parts of the world so I decided to leave the town and do what I wanted. It was quite difficult in the beginning, but as I traveled, the burdens of the past and future dissolved and I became a part of the present. I lived only in the now, and began to love life. Since I had nothing to lose I lived like I had never lived before. Instead of a quick death, I regained complete health. With my newfound knowledge of living in the now, life became remarkable and gratifying.

"As time went on, I devoted my life to living in the moment. I was even more successful, but never again did I give in to worries of the past or future. Everything in my life became in the now. I discovered that following my intuition, instead of doubting the power of awareness, made me happy and content."

I wondered if that was part of the riddle. After all, if he had listened to expert advice he would have died in bed. He was a wise man and I will remember the importance of this tale for the rest of my life. I know that when I sink into the sorrows of the past, I fall into a deep depression. I will commit myself to living in the now, as I see the importance of not dwelling on past sorrows and mistakes. An ugly face appeared in my mind: Udoki, the man who killed my family and friends. Did I have the power of enlightenment to forgive him? Never! I thought, as I felt an astounding anger in my heart. I pushed thoughts of him aside.

"Come, Shinhon," Shim said, "You will dine with me and later, please spend the night."

We had a pleasant night; the food was good and the conversation edifying. Later in the evening I was accompanied by a servant to a cozy room with a comfortable bed. As I dozed off, Shim's words ran through my mind. Then, I slept deep and sweet.

The Dream of Perspective

Once again I dreamed. In the dream I stood in front of two stairways. One led down to a place that looked dark and full of great despair, sadness, and hopelessness. I shuddered as I observed the great dark bleakness.

I looked to the other stairway that went up into a great light. I could not see the end of the stairs; they seemed to disappear into the light. I could feel the warmth on my face. It was the presence of goodness and joy. As I stood in front of the stairs I was awakened by the early morning crow of a rooster.

I got up to start my day and was given breakfast. I was told by an assistant that Shim had left for business reasons but that, Shem, his brother, was home and eager to see me.

I left the home of Shim with a newfound philosophy of living in the present. I was now aware that I was in control of the present and this feeling had an exhilarating and unrestricted effect on my soul. I knew that if I became overwhelmed with thinking of the past or future I could ground myself in the now. I knew that Now was all that really mattered.

I went across the pathway to the other house. I followed the path that zigzagged through the stunning garden, approaching Shem's front door.

Above his door was a sign that read, "The house of Shem — Attitude of a Good Life."

I knocked on the door and in a few moments it swung open. "Hello," a man shouted with a big smile on his face.

"Master Shinhon, please come in."

This man was quite different from Shim. He was younger and there was an incredible happy glow about him. His body was enormous in comparison to his brother, but he was not quite as tall. He was muscular and looked extremely strong. His face and countenance shown with friendliness and it made me want to be his friend immediately.

"I am so happy to see you," he said as he reached out and embraced me with both arms. I thought his hug might break me in two. It was comical for a stranger's greeting, but I felt that this man was a stranger to no one and lived the symbol of the "four" daily.

"Please come in and make yourself comfortable," he said. "I have been enjoying drinks and bread. I will bring you a plate and cup."

His home was quite a contrast to Shim's home. It was decorated with bright and brilliant colors of purple, yellow, and green. Everything in his home looked as if it had been created by an artisan. He laughed and talked as he showed me around. We came to a room with a large colored glass window where light came in from the outside. There were statues, paintings, and a huge library containing many books. I noticed that the furniture was also crafted in an expert and fine manner.

"Sit, and tell me about yourself," Shem said to me.

We talked and laughed for some time. Shem was so easy to talk to and it was fun just being around him. I thought to myself that there was no way anyone could be unhappy around this man.

I told him of the dream I had before I met his brother and the way he explained it to me.

"Yes, living in the now is very powerful," he said.

I told him I'd had another dream the night before. It was about two stairways and I proceeded to tell him how each one made me feel. The one going down was dark and wretched but the stairs going up were full of light and happiness. I asked him if he could tell me the meaning of the dream.

"Oh yes I can, young Shinhon, because I have lived that dream."

"The stairs going down are the constant negative thoughts in your mind. Every step down is a negative thought that is in our lives and we continue to feed the bad thoughts in our head. They will lead you down the stairs into complete hopelessness. But, with one loving and compassionate thought, you can take a step backward and get away from the dreary world below. As you focus on the good in life your thoughts will raise you up. I lived in that dreary world of despair at one time. I will never forget it."

I found it hard to believe that this jovial man could ever have lived in a world of sadness.

Shem continued speaking as I looked at him in fascination, "I had grown up always complaining and looking at what was wrong with the world. I only pointed out the unfairness in life and how dreadful things were.

"Those were dark days and it troubles me to talk about them now. I had no friends; had nothing to do with my brothers, and I believed life was a horrific joke from the Great Spirit. When I grew up, I had nothing. I became a beggar on the street. I was living in great despair at the bottom of the stairs. I realize now what a despicable place it was. When I could no longer go down the stairs, my life was horrible, unfair, and I was lost. Life was such a cruel joke to endure"

I could not believe he was speaking of himself. This man loved life with every fiber of his being.

He continued speaking, "One day as I lay in the street, barely able to move, a wise man came to the city. He had no legs, and one arm was missing. He was on the back of a large man. As they came down the street he saw me and asked his companion to stop.

'Hello,' he said politely to me.

"I looked up at this man. What an incredible smile, I thought. It made me feel warm inside. Here was a man with only one arm and no legs, who was a beaming light of happiness. I felt ashamed as I looked into this man's eyes. Here I was, a beggar on the street, feeling nothing but self-pity, when I had complete use of all my limbs.

"The wise man looked at me and asked, 'Tell me, sir, why is a strong young man like you begging on the streets?'

"I told him it was because life had been so unfair to me and that I was sorry I had been born. He asked his companion to put him down. He sat right beside me; his head tilted upward, taking in the sun's rays. Then he looked into my eyes with a most illuminating goodness. It hurt me to look at him as every part of his body seemed to glow with a light of love. After an agonizing time the wise man spoke, 'Listen well, my friend, as I have a profound gift for you.' He paused and then said, 'What you see is what you find.' With his one good hand, he reached into his pouch, pulled out an object, and gently placed it in my hand. It looked like a flower but was made of shimmering crystals. They were brilliant colors: green, red, bright white, blue, and purple. I wondered to myself how this had been crafted. It must be magic I thought. The crystals shone bright in the sunlight; the red of the petals shimmered like a million rubies. The stem was a bright emerald green. It was the most beautiful work of art I had ever seen."

Shem pointed to the mantel in the room. I got up and walked over to the mantel and there it was, as beautiful and bright as he described perhaps more so. It looked alive and lit the entire room with a soft glow. The glow may have been caused by the light in the room but I could not be sure.

Shem continued his story, "The wise man continued talking to me, Again he said, 'What you see is what you find, my young friend. Listen, and listen well. You see with your eyes first, then your mind disseminates what you are looking at. When you see only divine beauty, that message is sent to your soul and, as a result, you find divine beauty in your life.'

"The man motioned to be lifted and left me with his gift. I sat in the street for hours looking at the crystal flower. I was mesmerized by it. It was so beautiful that I focused on it, feeling nothing else existed. That night I made my way to the makeshift shelter I had built in the alleyways of the city. I caressed the flower all night, sleeping little, thinking most of the night about the wise man's statement.

"What you see is what you find.

"I thought about my life and how I had been dwelling on all the sad things. I sobbed as I thought about how I had squandered my existence looking at nothing but the wicked. That night I vowed to look at only the good in life. I awoke the next morning to a new world. The first thing I said to myself was, 'It is good to be alive.' My lungs are functioning and I have two legs to walk on. I walked through the city amidst the beauty with astonishment.

"As I passed people I looked for the beauty inside of them, when previously I had seen only jealousy and judgment, I now saw each person's magnificence. I was so used to people trying to avoid me that I was surprised by how many looked into my eyes and smiled at me. I said 'hello' and 'good morning' to everyone I saw. I realized I had a smile on my face. I ran to the river, eager to bathe as I loved the feel of the water on my body cleaning off the old me. I would never be the same again— of that I was sure."

The jolly man, Shem, looked at me with a great smile and continued, "Sometime later, after many adventures and fun in my life, I came to Ivicas and settled with my brothers in this beautiful place. Come, let me show you my home and the wonderful garden I have created. Then we will go into the village and I will show you the many farms that we work the year round."

Master Shem was so much fun to be around. He showed me to the garden and those who worked in it.

We ate lunch at one of the farms just outside of the village. Shem cooked for everyone on the farm. He was a great cook and it was fun to watch him laugh and talk to everyone as he cooked and served the entire meal. He told stories and was jovial. The farm people loved and accepted him as part of their families. He loved them as well.

The people from the surrounding area looked to Shem for advice. There was a farming drought in the area, and many were worried about their crops. One woman put her hand on Shem's shoulder and asked how long they could expect the drought to last.

With a big smile Shem said, "Don't you worry—the Great Spirit will provide."

Shem told me that it had been some time since it had rained but that the village had pulled together and obtained buckets of water from the river to keep the crops alive.

We visited the entire village and many farms. It was a remarkable community.

We returned to Shem's house in time for dinner. I was introduced to his wife, Tiv, and all seven children. I knew I would never remember all their names. Tiv was a beautiful generous woman who was as pleasant and jovial as her husband. We laughed and sang songs, making a lot of noise. The whole time I was in his house I had a smile on my face. As it was getting late I excused myself and went to bed. Tired from the day's activities, I slept almost immediately.

The Dream of Gratitude

That night I had another dream. I was in shackles, connected to a wall of rock. The shackles were tight around my wrists. Just out of reach was a table of great treasures, heaped on the entire length of the table. Around the treasures were piles of steaming hot food and ice cold cider. I had been there for a long time as I was gaunt, my skin wrinkling on my bones. I felt immense despair at my inability to obtain anything because I was shackled. Then, just as I thought I would die, the dream became a magnificent meadow of flowing grass and different colorful flowers. Before me was a massive banquet table, with cuisine fit for royalty. Around the table sat all the village people laughing and singing. They all looked at me and smiled, bidding me to sit at the head of the table.

Again I awoke to the sound of the rooster crowing. I got dressed and could not wait to tell Shem of the dream, but he was already gone for the day. His wife assisted me with a hot breakfast and good conversation. She told me that Shem's other brother, Shom, was looking forward to meeting me. Tiv said that Shom was the oldest brother and a very wise man. Tiv said she knew I would learn much from him.

After exercise and prayer I bid the people of the house of Shem farewell and set out for the house of Shom.

Above the door a carved sign announced: "The house of Shom— Attitude of Gratitude."

I knocked and after some time, the door was opened. I could tell his features were the same as the other men, but this man was much older than his brothers.

"I have been expecting you, young Shinhon," he said.

He was a tall slender man with a long beard that, hung to his waist and large hands with long fingers. Shom's dress was quite plain but meticulous.

He bid me to enter and grabbed my hand, wrapping an arm around my shoulder.

"Master Shinhon, it is so good to see you," Shom said.

He led me into his home, different from the others but beautiful in its own way. The walls were covered in dark wood with heavy grain. Massive beams ran across the ceiling. The architectural design was simple and clean, lightly decorated, a place where anyone would feel comfortable.

"Come, let us talk. How has your stay been so far?" he asked.

"It has been enlightening, Shom. Your brothers are wise men and I have learned much about life from them," I said.

He agreed. "Yes, we have all made an effort to live happily in this life."

We sat in a large room on huge purple pillows; underneath was a decorated carpet with intricate designs.

I told him what I had learned from his brothers and the dreams I had.

"You had another profound dream, I think?" said Shom.

"Yes," I answered with a little surprise in my voice.

I told him of my latest dream.

"Very good," he said. He folded his arms and bowed his head for a moment, meditating on the meaning of my dream, and then he said, "The first part of the dream is where our thoughts chain us down; we believe and see only what we lack in our lives. As we focus on limited thoughts, we shackle our lives by negative beliefs. The shackles keep us from moving forward, even though all of our dreams and desires are in front of us, just out of reach, because we do not believe that we are worthy, or we think life has dealt us unfairly. So many times we see the beauty in the world and ask ourselves why everyone has so much in life and we have nothing." He shook his head and looked sad for a moment. "The wall a person builds in his mind is a symbol of all of the corruption in this world. As we lock into everyday incidents and think that is all there is, we bind ourselves tighter and tighter to the wall."

I knew what he said was the truth.

He continued, "The other part is to see all that there is to be grateful for in this life. When only the good is considered, even when some things do not go as expected, the focus of your thoughts shift and life is a banquet. As you possess gratitude for the people in your life you will be surrounded by those who love you. As you look at the great feast of goodness in your life and honor it, goodness will cover you like a warm blanket and you will be blessed tenfold. Gratitude for your blessings is a call to the universe to give more." Shom's face turned serious. He put his hand on my shoulder as we sat and then he spoke again, "Shinhon, I once considered myself a learned man. I devoted my life to learning everything. I obtained my education so I could be better and smarter than everyone else. Soon I began to think of nothing but what I didn't have. I felt I was wronged at every turn. I began to see only the deceitfulness of others. I felt that everyone was out to cheat me. I trusted no one. All I could see was that I did not possess what I deserved in life. I was angry with the world. Here I was, a learned man, and yet I was neither respected nor wealthy. I was chained to the wall of ungratefulness and all the riches and happiness of life seemed to be out of my reach. I did not comprehend why I had so little."

A servant came in and offered us drinks. As we sat, Shom continued, "I was working for a wealthy merchant, taking stock in the storehouse. I also took care of the shop and sold merchandize to customers. I hated the job and most of all I hated the people. I hated and envied that rich merchant, feeling I deserved much more than he did. I thought I was smarter and worthy of more. I had no friends and no one wanted to be around me. I lived in a small shack behind the store, where I sat and wallowed in self-hatred. I read about things that did not matter."

Shom paused for a moment. "One day I decided that I would go into the wilderness and live alone, or maybe just die there. Life was unfair and not worth living. But, before I could leave, a man and a little girl came into the shop. He and the child were both filthy. He asked for the price of a loaf of bread. I impatiently told him the cost of each type of bread. As we bartered over the bread, the young girl stood staring at the candy jar on the counter. She looked in wonder at the many different kinds of candies—the bright colors and interesting shapes. The man looked at his child. I saw a sad longing in his face. The little girl pointed at the candy and her father knew it would cost more than he could afford. He asked me how much the one piece on a long stick cost. I knew that particular piece of candy was more than the bread. I looked at the angelic face of the little girl. Occasionally, I had taken many of those tasty candies for myself. This was the first time that I could remember feeling real compassion. I told the father that today we were giving candy for each loaf of bread sold."

I looked at Shom as he talked. He had such a look of love and goodness on his face. I found it difficult to believe this man could have been the way he described himself.

He continued talking, "I did not know the circumstances of the father and child but I could tell by their countenance that life had been hard. It seemed more than they should have had to endure. The father knew I was not telling the truth and that I was being kind to his little girl. Tears rippled down his cheecks. I remember his thank you so filled with love and gratitude that I was taken back. I felt warmth in my heart for the first time in a long while. I was amazed by the light that shone on the girl's face as she sheepishly took the candy from me. Such joy, love, and wonder radiated from this child, my feelings melted in an instant. She picked up one of the long stick candies and grasped it in her tiny hand. I was astonished by her beauty. She did not gulp the candy down but only stood there looking at the stick and basking with love that it was hers. The sound of her father's 'Thank You,' washed over me like a wave from the sea, drowning me in a flood of emotion."

Shom's eyes became glassy with tears as he relived that moment. "I was pondering over what had happened as they left the store. It was the first time I had looked at a customer or felt any emotion. The picture of that child, transformed into an angel by a piece of candy, and the father filled with so much gratitude over such a simple thing. I sat in the store and cried as waves of enlightenment flooded through me. I looked back at my life and thought of how much time I had wasted by always reflecting on what I did not have, unmindful of what I did have."

Shom could not hold back the tears as they rolled down his checks. He continued, "In that moment my whole life changed." He whispered, "Thank you for this new life. Thank you for what I have learned about the love and gratitude of a father and the great joy of a small child."

The sweet man put a hand up to his check and wiped the tears away. "From that day forward, I gave thanks, showed gratitude every day for my many blessings, and only looked at the beauty of life, I became the merchant's greatest asset and the store did more business than ever. People came from all around to obtain insight from me. I became known as a great and wise man.

After some time the merchant grew old and having no children, he gave his business to me."

Shom gained his composure and said, "Gratitude is the magic that makes our dreams and wishes come true, but the poison of ingratitude can bring your greatest nightmares."

Shom told me that he reunited with his brothers, who had also established great insight into life. They moved to the village of their birth and now manage the city with happiness and love.

I was mystified by the great power of this humble man. I found it hard to believe that he had ever been a bitter and unhappy person. He asked me to come and be with him and his brothers for the village meeting.

We talked some more about life and I shared my learning of the wisdoms as we ate lunch and prepared for the meeting.

Thoughts in Practice

We went to the middle of the village where the meeting was scheduled. On the east side stood three chairs and on two of them sat Shim and Shem. The last chair was Shom's. I talked with Shim and Shem. They were happy to see me. Many people began to gather. It looked like the whole village had assembled for the meeting. There was much commotion. The people seemed worried about something but the ruling brothers were not shaken.

The brothers called the meeting to order and introduced me. Most of the people had heard of me and my travels. The crowd grew excited.

One of the village people spoke, "There has been no rain for some time. We work much harder to bring water to the land."

Buckets of water from the river were not sufficient to keep their crops alive and the villagers felt they could not continue without rain.

The brothers listened as each person came up to speak of their worries.

I began to gain some insight. A vision started to form in my head. I continued listening to the people, as I thought of Shim, Shem, and Shom, and what I had learned from them.

I asked for permission to talk, pointing out the greatness of Shim, Shem, and Shom, and what I had learned from them. No doubt the villagers had also learned from them because the wise men lived their philosophy.

I explained to them that I had an idea that could assist them with their plight. We could not wait for rain, as Shim would say, we must do something now.

A woman from the crowd asked, "What can we do?"

"What good can we perceive?" I asked. "We can see the situation as good or bad. According to Shem we could see the good even though there was no rain. We could see good in the knowledge that we have an unlimited abundance of water. The great river is close to the farms."

"Yes," one of the men said, "We have been working so hard to bring the water to the land, but it is very difficult and as the weather gets hotter we don't know if we can keep on without rain."

I spoke, "I understand, but if you did not have the river, all would be lost. So you should see the great blessing of the river."

The man replied with hopelessness in his voice, "Yes, but if it does not rain, we will not have enough water."

I raised my hands and shouted to the villagers, "Shom has taught me that we have the choice to see what we do not have, like rain. No rain means this land will eventually die. If we continue to focus on this vision, then yes, your lands will be lost. What we must consider is how grateful we should be that the river is here. It contains all the water we need, and could use, to wash over this land."

"The river runs through the city but not on the land," someone in the crowd said.

I again raised my hands and said, "Yes, but those of you who have heard of me must know that I am an expert builder, and as I look at the great river, my thoughts are that there could be many small rivers running off the great Momotha and into the fields."

"That is a dream," a man said, "do you think we could pray to the gods for a lightning bolt to dig a river. I say we should pray for rain before hoping for a miracle of rivers?"

I spoke with authority as I said, "No, we will act now and dig the rivers. I have a design in my head, and an idea for creating the small rivers. I have a plan to build a dam so we can flood different parts of the fields, like the beavers."

There was lots of stirring in the crowd and conversation about ideas. Then I spoke again. "If you give me a few days to walk over the land and the river I will come up with a strategy. I think we could do this and you would never have to worry about water for the crops again. As long as the great river runs, it will be fed by the prodigious mountains to the north."

Suddenly as the people began to comprehend what I was saying, there was a lot of talk and much excitement. The brothers discussed the solution with each other and then Shom spoke. "The Master has sent this great man to assist us. We will give him everything he needs and do what he asks."

Again, the crowd was excited and a wave of encouragement charged through them.

Shom spoke. "We will give Shinhon some time to put a plan in place and then we will work to make it happen."

We spent a great deal of time talking and I was given some farm workers who would be assisting me. I asked if I could look over the fields again and map out the river. I spent the night with Shom, and we talked about my plans and how it would look. We drew a draft of the river and crops, showing the best area to dig trenches.

The next day I scouted out the area, and with a strong determination and vision, I started to draw plans that would work for the small rivers. It took many months and the work was hard. We started from the fields and worked our way to the river, digging trenches for the water. Animals were used to assist in digging the small waterways. We made an intricate path, connecting and weaving through the fields. The people had to bring water to the fields to keep them from drying up and they also had to dig. At night I counseled with the brothers and learned a lot about the power of thought.

As we arrived at the river I planned how to make a dam connected to a lever, so the villagers could control the water flow. After many months of work, it was time to start the rivers. Word was out that the great Shinhon was creating miracles in the village of Ivicas. People came from all over the land to observe for themselves and everyone was eager to help the villagers.

When the lever was opened, water began to flow. It was an incredible sight: All the tributaries began to fill up. One by one, water flowed to each farming area. The children ran to catch up with the water and people jumped in and rode on the water. In no time the waters had run their course.

It was a great miracle. There was a feast and celebration. The brothers spoke, "This day will be remembered forever as the celebration of the rivers. We will always remember you, Master Shinhon. "You are a miracle and a gift to this city."

Shom said with great humility, "Thank you, Master Shinhon. I give you all of the pure gratitude in me."

The Answer to the Riddle

I stayed in the city of Ivicas with the people and the brothers for some time, making certain all was well. Then one day I felt an urgency to return to the palace of the Master. I knew it was time to bid farewell to this wonderful village, the three wise men, and all the happy and prosperous villagers.

I said my farewells to the villagers and the brothers, all of whom I had grown to love. Then I left on a caravan traveling north.

I had been gone for many months, but finally I was back at the palace of the Master. The guards bowed to me now. "Master Shinhon," they said as they saw me. I was welcomed with no questions asked.

The Master was sitting in his great hall.

"Young Shinhon, welcome back. I am so glad to see you again."

"I am happy to be back, Master. It is good to see you too." was my reply.

With a serious look, he asked, "Shinhon, do you know the answer to the riddle I gave you?"

"Yes, I do, Master." I said.

I then recited the riddle and gave him my answer. "What is always with you—at sad times and at mad times, at happy times and at joyful times? If you do your best to push away, it will stay longer, no matter what you do or say. If you laugh or cry it will obey if you feed it, you will become it. It can assist you in moving mountains or stop you from lifting a grain of sand."

"It is all in the power of our thoughts and the actions we take to see the blessings in our lives. The answer to the riddle is thoughts, Master. What we think, is what we become. The many thoughts we have each day, generate all of our realities for good or naught. We can change what we think with one positive thought. Nothing is written in stone. Life, like our thoughts, is in flux every minute of the day. When an ugly thought rears its head, change it to a good one, so it does not stay."

The Master said, "Yes, my young apprentice, indeed it is our thoughts that create our realities. You have learned the wisdom well. You have learned much, Shinhon; you have learned well as my pupil and have matured so much from the angry boy you were when you first entered my palace."

WISDOM

6

"*Better than a thousand hollow words, is one word that brings peace.*"

BUDDHA

The Court

I remained and talked with the Master for hours, discussing the philosophies of the wisdoms I had learned.

The Master spoke, "For the next wisdom you are to stay with me for a year in the palace. I hold court every week, listening to the people of the land and assisting them with their needs. You will observe these conversations and at the end of the year I want you to inform me of the wisdom you have witnessed. Now, get cleaned up and do what you will, as the palace is your home."

That night I lay in bed thinking over my life and how grateful I was for finding a reason for my existence. I had gone through so much to be in this place and live with the Master. I had no idea how exhausted I was as my eyes closed.

I woke up in the morning ready to start the day. I started with prayer. I had gained a strong relationship with the Great Spirit. I always remembered to stress my body every day. My soldier training was perfect and I ran when I could. I got dressed and ate a light breakfast with the servants. Then I strolled through the gardens. I had no idea how much deeper one could meditate by walking around the mazes. It seemed as though I was in an altered state of consciousness. I felt closer to the spirit than ever.

Later I practiced my exercises, finding I could not let a day go by without them. The meditation enhanced my workout.

I pondered over my thoughts of Shim, Shem, and Shom. I saw the importance of my contemplations and made a commitment to do all I could to keep my thoughts true to the new direction I had discovered in my life. I live in the now; looking for the good things in life, grateful for all I have. I was happy to see Mehi as she interrupted my thoughts.

She was now head of the palace servants and worked hard keeping everything clean and orderly. I had watched her work and talked with her many times. She was a good and loving woman. She will always have a place in my heart for the kindness shown to me when I was just a dirty young boy coming to see the Master.

"Master Shinhon," Mehi said. "The Master will see you in court today." She smiled and winked at me. I admired her cheerfulness and liked her very much,

"Wonderful," I told her.

"Master Shinhon, you have grown so much and become quite a man since arriving at the palace so many years ago. I have watched you and know you are a good man."

"Thank you Mehi, I have noticed you as well. You are a loving and caring woman."

She smiled and we both laughed. As she picked up her laundry basket she turned to me and said, "Now, you must now get ready for court, Shinhon. I have laid out your clothing for you."

"Do they fit or are they your son's?" I laughed thinking of the first clothes she had given me so many years ago.

I put the clothes on and they fit. This was going to be much nicer then traveling for days to some far off city.

I met with the Master in the great hall. There was much commotion and many were there just to see the Master in court. I was surprised as I thought we would be alone.

The Master pointed to a comfortable chair for me to sit in. "Are you ready for your first court experience? There is always a lot of business and many problems to solve for the people of this land."

The Master turned away from me and looked toward the people in audience saying, "Humanity communicates through words. Action is the way you communicate inside yourself through feelings and thoughts, and they are connected to the words you speak and think. You will understand that words are powerful and how you use them makes all the difference."

I nodded in understanding, thinking about what the Master said.

The Master continued, "The words we speak are the building blocks of our lives. Our thoughts define us, but the action of the words we put in our mind creates our thoughts. The wisdom of words is associated with the thoughts that run through our minds, whether they are good or bad."

I knew what the Master said was true and believed it with every fiber of my being.

He looked at me and said, "All wisdoms connect with each other in some form as they are the secrets to mastering a noble life."

I replied, "I will pay close attention to the words that are spoken, Master."

The Master said, "You will comprehend the wisdom as you study and listen to members of the court and as we all communicate with each other—some better than others. You will learn to scrutinize faces, identifying their truth as well as their body language. The way people converse creates their personal lives, minute by minute."

There were many people in the court. Guards were there for protection to keep matters in line and others from the high court took their rightful places by the Master.

The guard closest to the Master consulted with the people as they came forward. There were so many disputes and I admired the guard's patience. The Master listened intently as the guard announced each individual.

There were many property disputes; people who had felt wronged and cheated by their landlord or neighbor. There were many unhappy husbands and wives who were no longer in love and wished for dissolution of their marriage. Problem after problem was brought before the Master, and he listened, never raising his voice or showing any signs of disappointment. He dispensed justice with a keen eye and precise words.

I paid close attention while watching people's body language and facial expressions.

Lie or Die

Later in the day, three men came to consult with the Master. The Master asked them, "What is the purpose of your visit?"

One of the three men identified himself as Shemal, an old man, who said, "Master, I am the mayor of the city of Shikil to the east of your land. I have ruled Shikil for a long time. I am old and it is time for me to turn the leadership over to a new ruler. These two men have been great leaders of the community of Shikil and both wish to be the mayor. I trust each man implicitly and know that either one would do the job well. They have been talking in the streets, trying to persuade the people to pick one of them and now the city is divided. I brought the men to you to help me choose one of them since my city was once a happy place and is now politically separated."

The Master asked the two men to stand before him. He looked at the first man. "Why should you be leader of the city?" He said,

The first man spoke, "My name is Miy and I have lived in the city all my life. I have been a well known merchant and am respected in the community. I have counseled with the mayor on many issues and we have become great friends. Shemal trusts my advice."

The man explained why he felt he would be a good mayor for the city. He was simple and his speech was not eloquent, but there was an honest sincerity about him. When he was finished talking, the Master turned to the other man and asked the same question."

The second man began to speak, "I am Yoshiani, and have also lived in the city all my life and am well respected." The man was vociferous as he began to complain about all the things wrong with Miy and told of his lies and underhanded deeds. He painted a bad picture of this man. It was hard to believe what he said about the other person. He was convincing and after he finished talking there was great doubt about the man, Miy.

"Do you have anything to say about these allegations?" The Master asked looking at Miy.

Miy answered, "Yes, Yoshiani is known for his destructive words and is also hypocritical, but the people residing in our city know I am a fair and just man."

The Master was thoughtful for some time, then turned to the man, Yoshiani, and asked. "What is the most powerful way to change a man's thoughts, a stick to the head or words?"

The man Yoshiani said without hesitation. "A stick to the head would quickly change a man's perceptions and is a more powerful persuader; words are only for communication."

"I see." said the Master.

The Master said, "I have made my decision, I will have the man, Miy, killed at sunrise and Yoshiani will be the new mayor of the city of Shikil."

Complete silence fell over the court. All three men were stunned and had looks of total surprise on their faces. I was also shocked by the Master as his response seemed quite harsh.

The Master said, "Please send the next person before me."

Before they left the man Yoshiani asked the Master if he would please wait. "I do not want to see Miy killed as we have grown up together and I care for him and his family."

The Master spoke sharply. "Yes, perhaps that is so, but you stated that he was a liar and deceiver and the city would be better without him."

Yoshiani pleaded with the Master and soon was in tears. "Master, maybe I exaggerated this man's dishonesty." Yoshiani lowered his head and sobbed. "I wanted to paint an ugly picture of him so he would look bad and I would appear to be the better man for mayor."

The master replied, "Your words were strong against Miy, and I only know him from the words you have spoken."

Yoshiani wept harder and shame showed in his face.

"You understand," said the Master, "that if I had known this man and knew of his goodness, and if he had been a friend to me, anyone could have taken a stick to my head and I would have died before saying otherwise of him. But, words can put doubt in another's mind, whether true or false."

The Master looked away and said, "Miy will die in the morning. I have no time for your words. Let's continue to hear the next in line."

"Please, Master," Yoshiani said. "I confess; I have lied against Miy. He is a good man. I wish to take his place tomorrow, as I deserve to be executed. I have done a great injustice to this man for my own personal gain. I have known him all my life and he is just and good. I am the evil one who should be punished. Please, Master," he said as he fell to the floor sobbing.

The Master's voice softened and he spoke to Yoshiani. "I ask you again which is more powerful to change a man's thoughts: a stick to the head or a word? You lied about this man but after hearing my sentence of death, which is one word, you now say you would die for him."

The man bowed his head and said. "I never understood the great power of words, Master. I have carelessly tossed words around my whole life to get what I wanted."

The Master looked at all three of the men and said, "You are to go back to your city and contemplate what happened today. I believe that now you will be able to choose the leader for your people."

Succeed or Fail
What is The Word

I was in the palace for many days. It was enlightening to observe the Master in the court. I found it interesting to listen to him solve and defuse the problems of his land. I could feel the love and respect he had for his people. The power of the Master's words was sometimes shocking.

I became close to Mehi. She was a good person and like so many great people I had met and learned from, she too, was much older. She told me about her life and I told her about mine and what I had learned from the wisdoms. She said my words gave her awareness and insight. She said she had a good life as she spoke of her children and husband. She felt she had been blessed in life.

I enjoyed my stay at the palace and looked forward to the time I spent at court every week.

One day a man came before the Master saying, "Master, I know not what to do. I have tried to succeed so many times but I am a failure. I have tried many things and yet failed. My family is wealthy and they live to the north. I continue failing at everything I try. I need your help to comprehend why I keep failing. Master, I bow before you asking for your assistance in understanding. Please help me."

The Master looked down at the young man and asked, "What have you done in your life, and why do you feel you are unsuccessful?"

Jiao, as he called himself, began to weep. I felt sorry for him, but for some reason he irritated me. He had all his faculties, health, and potential, yet he was in a constant state of self-pity.

"I have tried merchandising and farming, I tried to be a family man but have failed in everything I've tried to do."

Every time this man opened his mouth I felt more irritated.

"You have not answered my question," said the Master. "The question is, what have you done, not what have you tried?"

I smiled to myself.

The man looked bewildered. "I am confused, Master," Jiao said.

The Master took a small scroll from under his robe and threw it in front of the man.

The Master said, "Please, I ask you to **try** to pick up that scroll and hand it to me."

The man grabbed the scroll from the ground and handed it to the master.

The Master again threw the scroll before the man. "That is not what I asked you to do," said the Master. "I told you to **try** to pick up the scroll. I did not say pick it up and give it to me. I just asked you to **try**." The Master said the word *try* slowly and more pronounced.

Jiao looked puzzled and said. "I do not understand you, Master."

The Master said to Jiao in an intense voice. "Have you ever tried and succeeded at anything?"

Cowering, he said, "I tried to come and see you Master and I have done so."

The Master looked at him and smiled. "You did not **try** to see me. You traveled here and you did see me. There was no *try*. The word **try** is powerful and can destroy entire kingdoms. The words, 'I will *try*,' from the lips of a leader usually signify failure. There is only *do,* there is no *try*, if you want to succeed. It is the same as saying, I will fail, and cannot succeed. I will never reach my goals. **Try** is an infection of inactivity."

I was exhilarated.

The Master continued, "When the word **try** is used has success followed? No, **try** is only followed with failure. If you were successful you would use the words, "I did it." People throw words around as though they have no power but they are filled with magic. **Try** is a powerful word for failure, just like *do* is a powerful word for success."

Jiao still looked puzzled as he said, "Help me understand, Master"

The Master continued, "Help is another powerful word used to freeze growth. If you were drowning in quicksand and thought you would surely die, you would scream, 'Help me, help me.' It is because at that moment you are in total despair and you know that without help from someone you will die. If someone hears you they will know you are in distress and save you. You see the word **help** is a powerful component assuring that nothing the person can do for themselves and they are at the mercy of others to save them. While sinking in quick sand, helping you is justified. The word **help** may alert whoever hears it and they will do everything in their power to save you."

Jiao looked deep into the Master's eyes, confused, but pondering over what he was saying.

In a strong voice the Master said, "The problem appears to me that you use this word not because you are dying but because it is a crutch for your own inadequacies. In almost every situation if you ask for help and wait for others to give you a hand it can cripple you. If we need someone's help, but do not wish to have our own power taken away we would ask for assistance. The word assist forms a partnership with others. To get **assistance** is not letting go of your responsibilities and being at the mercy of others."

I observed that Jiao was beginning to understand.

The Master put out his hand and said, "You see, if I put my hand out and ask for **assistance**, there is a different energy than if I put my hand out and ask for **help**."

The Master looked at the man and said, "You have learned the power of TRY and HELP very well."

Jiao shook his head, analyzing what the Master was telling him.

"You came to me this day to ask how I could **help** you **try** to stop your failures, yes?"

"Yes, Master," Jiao said.

The Master stood up from his chair and spoke in a loud voice, "Then do not insist on **trying** and wanting **help**. Go and **do** something, and if you want help from others, ask for assistance unless you are helpless and drowning, then help is a true powerful word that could save your life. Asking for assistance will position you with the person you are asking in a partnership."

Jiao smiled for the first time since his arrival.

"Go home and keep *doing* and you will succeed," the master said. "Remember, 'I try, I will try, and I tried' should no longer be a part of your vocabulary."

The man left with a look of bewilderment on his face.

I could see the wisdom in the words of the Master, and agreed with the power of his words, yet, I did not see that this man understood. I thought of the wisdom of learning. If we are not in tune with ourselves and ready for new lessons they can slip through our awareness.

The Master noticed that I was in deep thought. "What is troubling you, young apprentice?"

"I was thinking over what just happened, Master."

The Master looked at me and said, "There was a seed of wisdom planted in that man. Now it is up to him whether he will cultivate it or let it die. In the future, when he says the words *try* and *help* he will remember what was spoken here today. He will think of the great distance he traveled to get this answer from me and that will assist him throughout his life, if he chooses. We are in this world to learn with our own free agency to choose whether to make it hard or easy. We learn either way."

The Poison and the Antidote

I spent a lot of time in the gardens of the palace in meditation and prayer. As I pondered what I was learning with the Master, the wisdom of *words* came to me. Words can be compared to a powerful weapon, to defend or defeat. Thus, I had learned a new meaning for the importance of our words and realized that words are thoughts in action.

Just as I finished meditating, I saw Mehi. I looked forward to talking with her. I enjoyed my time with her and we had become good friends. Even with the age difference we were close. In some ways—many ways— she reminded me of my mother. I had great respect for her.

Months passed and there were a few occasions when the Master let me administer the court. I had become quite well known and respected. It seemed incredible how the words of others could reveal the true individual.

One day a man and a young lady, his daughter, stood before us in court. The man introduced himself as Lowling. He introduced his beautiful daughter, as Shushan. They came from a farm northwest of the palace.

"Go on, Lowling, what may I do for you and your daughter?" the Master asked.

"I fear I have destroyed Shushan. She no longer speaks, saying very little if anything."

Shushan looked melancholy.

"Do you know why she does not talk?" asked the Master.

The man looked down and ashamedly said, "Yes, I am afraid it is because of me. A few years ago when my daughter was quite young, I had a devastating loss with my corn and wheat crops. They were destroyed by drought and I was worried about what I would do. I came in from a stressful day in the fields, feeling tired and worried about my family's future. My head was pounding from all the stress and worry. I was in our small home pondering my dilemma. My daughter, Shushan, came into the house singing and dancing, happy as a child could be. With my head pounding and my mind racing, I yelled as loud as I could:

"Shut up, Shushan! Shut up! No one wants to hear your ugly voice. **Shut up!**"

A tear ran down the man's face as he said, "I knew as soon as the words came out of my mouth I shouldn't have said them. It was wrong but I was too engulfed in my own worries to care about hurting her feelings."

He wiped his tears on a handkerchief and continued. "She quit singing that moment and has never sung again. She had always been a happy child, but after that day she changed. She was cautious about what she said and did. Master, I am devastated at how I changed my daughter from a happy loving girl, to a child who is now afraid to speak."

The master looked down at the young girl. She lowered her eyes. "Is it true what your father has said, that you are unhappy and afraid to speak around others?"

She looked up at the Master and nodded her head.

"Do you know that your father loves you and feels bad about what he said and did?"

Again she shook her head in agreement.

The Master stood from his chair and went over to the young girl asking, "Since that time it is hard for you to talk and sing?"

She nodded her head in agreement.

The Master looked around the court, his eyes finding Lowling. "I have spoken many times in the court concerning the power of words. Words can heal or wound, especially those we love and cherish. This child has been poisoned with your words and now suffers from the venom. You and your daughter are invited to stay in the palace tonight and tomorrow there is someone I want her to meet."

That night with Mehi's assistance we gave the man and his daughter, Shushan, food and the warmest, most comfortable place in the palace.

I was curious about who the Master had in mind.

The Master declared that the next day there would be a special event for Lowling and Shushan.

He told Mehi to make arrangements for the evening events. She complied with his request. She and the servants would do anything for him.

The day was full of preparations as delicious epicurean delights were prepared; the servants, gardeners, and cooks, had been hustling and bustling around the palace since early that morning. I walked through the garden maze and talked with the Master when I got a chance, as he was meditating. I asked him why he was spending so much time on the man and his daughter.

He said the child had been poisoned, and that she let the poison take over her entire life. She needed an antidote if she was to ever be happy again.

That night the great hall was decorated in a festive manner and many had been invited to partake of the feast and entertainment. There were some comical jugglers that at times almost made Shushan laugh.

As I watched the jugglers, I thought back to the day my village was destroyed and the time I had taken in the city watching the jugglers. Then I remembered wanting to be a juggler myself. That was long ago and I have become more than a juggler. The jugglers were fun, but I felt an intense pain watching them.

The Master stood up. "I have a great treat for everyone today. We have an entertainer from the city and she is willing to perform for us, in honor of our guests. We are privileged to hear Leli, the singer who graciously accepted my invitation. The Master clapped and from behind him, a woman stepped out of one of the doorways of the great hall.

I had never seen this person before. I knew I would have remembered her; she was the most beautiful woman I had ever seen; she possessed soul-deep beauty that shone with a magical light of love and splendor. Her porcelain skin made her black hair shine like a pool of deep water. She moved as graceful as an elegant swan on a glass lake. Her hair was tied with a soft ribbon trailing down her back. Her dark penetrating eyes looked as if she could see into your soul. I would not be surprised if she could—she was a mystical person, like a goddess.

She bowed to everyone and said, "Thank you for the opportunity to entertain you today. I would like to dedicate a song to all of you."

Everyone in the room was captivated by her beauty. She began to sing and it was as if an angelic being had been sent down by the Great Spirit. I could see some people crying and others just watched, loving the performance before them.

She sang for quite some time. Everyone was enjoying her music and no one wanted her to stop. The way she moved when she sang suggested that if the world ended in this moment everyone would die happy.

As she finished dancing and singing she bowed and said to the Master, "Thank you for the opportunity to sing." For a time we were all taken aback by her beauty. The Master broke the spell by starting to clap. We all joined in with a roar of applause.

After the musical number the Master asked Leli to sit with us and enjoy the rest of the night. He introduced Lowling and Shushan to the beautiful woman and she sat down by Shushan. Conversation ensued, but everyone in the room was still drawn to the incredible woman.

Leli looked at the girl with loving and kind eyes, "Did you enjoy the show?" she asked.

"Very much," Shushan said. Her eyes filled with amazement as she added, "You are very beautiful."

"Thank you," Leli said, "You are very beautiful yourself." Her smile made you want to please her.

Leli continued speaking, "The Master told me that you do not talk much. Is that true?" The girl, Shushan, looked somewhat sad and with her face looking down she nodded her head in agreement. "The Master told me a little of your dilemma, so I understand. I know how destructive harsh words can be and wounding to the soul. It is difficult to get over another's insensitive words. Sometimes words are spoken without thinking about the damage they might do to others." Shushan gazed at her again with a puzzled look on her face.

I also felt bewilderment at the thought of anyone saying something harsh to this breathtaking woman.

Leli continued, "I was born on the streets and soon after my birth my mother left me for dead." Everyone looked stunned, wondering how a mother could do that to her own child. "I was found in the streets and placed in an orphanage. When I was older, the nurse in charge told me that I was the ugliest child the caretakers had ever seen. She was an evil woman and wielded great poisonous power with her words."

Everyone was astonished at what Leli said. That cannot be true, I thought. How could this woman ever be considered ugly?

Leli spoke again. "I was raised in the orphanage, teased and taunted by the other children because of my ugliness. When I got older I ran away and lived on the streets. Anywhere was better than the orphanage,"

As they listened everyone shook their heads in disbelief.

She continued, "I did what I could to earn a living and take care of myself. I always kept my face hidden. I begged on the streets for some time. Then I was lucky enough to find a job at a small laundry where I was left alone outside in the back of the shop washing clothing. I felt safe and protected. I was given a small shack to live in close to where I worked. I went out as little as possible because I did not want others to see me. I felt that I looked like a monster. I believed the people at the orphanage and the words they had told me all my young life.

"But there was some joy in the back alone, washing the clothes. I found my voice and loved singing as I worked. I would never sing around others. I washed clothes and sang, content to live my life that way forever."

Leli took the ribbon out of her hair, letting it cascade down her back and shoulders. Her beauty left me breathless with astonishment. Then, she said, "I was startled one day by a young merchant who came to the back of the building and asked me if I was the person he had heard singing. I felt ashamed and tried covering my face to hide. He persisted, asking me again if the voice that drew him to this place was mine? He told me he had never heard anyone sing so beautifully. I told him, "Yes, but I will not be a nuisance and sing again. I told him I was sorry for disturbing him. The man grabbed me, holding both of my arms and told me he wished I would never stop! He said my singing was the most beautiful thing he had ever heard. At first he thought he heard angels singing, and then was drawn to my voice."

There was a smile on her face as she recounted the event. "He took off my hood and looked into my eyes. He was a handsome man and his eyes gleamed with great love and compassion. He told me that I was a beautiful woman and had an angelic voice to match my beauty. My heart stung as I asked why he was mocking me. I put my hood back on and asked him why he would make fun of one so ugly as I and if he had been sent as a cruel joke? He explained that he did not understand as he grabbed me and looked into my eyes. Then he spoke to me again repeating that he had never seen anyone as beautiful I."

Her eyes shined as if she was a supernatural being as she continued speaking. "The conviction in his voice melted my heart. I felt instant love for this man and my past taunts and troubles dissolved with his words. He took me away and we were married. The words of this handsome young merchant changed me forever. He is now my world and I am his."

"I sing in great halls to many who love and enjoy my performance," she said. "I have never been called ugly again." All who listened were astounded by her story. There was a look of total bewilderment on the young girl, Shushan's face.

Leli spoke to Shushan. "You are also so beautiful," she said lovingly as she put her arms around Shushan. "I know you have a voice to match your beauty. Will you let me instruct you and assist in bringing out that beautiful voice? It would be my pleasure to give you powerful words put to music to show how grateful I am for all that I have, and I want to share it with you."

Shushan was shy but nodded her head once again in agreement, and said in a soft voice, "I will be ever so grateful to you, Leli, thank you."

As the days went by the palace was filled with music. The young girl, Shushan, began singing with Leli, and became a different person. She was no longer the shy timid girl who first arrived at the palace. I could be content listening to their sweet voices forever.

I felt regret as the time came for Shushan to leave the palace. The poison had melted from her body and mind, and now she was a loving and alive young woman, ready for a good life. My year in the palace was ending. I enjoyed the court and had been blessed by living in the palace. I was truly grateful for my life. In the back of my mind I knew I would never forget my family and the love of my mother and father. I was grateful for what I had learned.

Words of Life

One night as I talked with Mehi, we discussed the wonderful wisdom of words. I told her I had never thought of how powerful they could be.

With a solemn look, she bowed her head and said, "I know firsthand the power of words. Earlier in my life four words saved me from death."

She was always such a happy woman. But now her voice was soft and melancholy, almost shame-like.

She looked to the ground as she talked, "I was young and married to a good man. We were given a parcel of land and worked hard. It took us many years to cultivate the ground. It was hard work but we managed to live and during this time I gave birth to a baby boy. A few years after our child was born, my husband became ill. There was nothing anyone could do for him. He passed away and I was devastated. Not only because I loved him dearly, but I had no idea how to run a farm and take care of my baby at the same time. I went into a deep depression. I was terrified for my son as our supplies were running out."

I reached over and took her hand as the tears welled up in her eyes with remembrance.

She continued, "At the lowest point, I decided I could not live and would take my life. I was oblivious to all around me. I only wanted to die. The words in my head were an evil poison that I could not control.

"I reached for a knife and was prepared to take my life. Despair is a powerful emotion. Just at that moment of deepest sorrow when I was ready to end it all, I heard four words.

"Mama, I need you."

I put my arm around her as she sobbed at the thoughts of that horrific time.

Through her tears she exclaimed, "My child was frightened and alone. My little son looked up at me as though he knew what was happening. I put the knife down, feeling guilty beyond words. I told him our life would be better, somehow. I felt stronger as I thought of my child and not just my own despair. I held my son close and hugged and kissed him for a long time as tears ran down my face. With those four words a spell had been broken. I focused on my son and knew we would survive. It was difficult to scratch out an existence and soon we had to leave the farm, but I came to the palace where the Master offered me a job as a servant. It has been many years and I have had a good life with another wonderful husband and other children. My son became a great and well respected man."

Mehi looked into my eyes and said, "I know the power of words. If you live the power of your words, my brave Shinhon, your life and the entire world will open up to you."

I loved this woman so much. I would miss her. I knew the time had arrived and I would be moving on to the next wisdom.

Words

I enjoyed my time in the palace and learned so much, but I knew when I was called to see the Master that my visit was finished.

As once again I stood before the Master, he asked: "What have you learned about this wisdom, in your year of living at the palace with me?"

I answered his question, "I can see that the wisdom of *words* is a powerful and empowering phenomenon; observing in the court gave me ample insight into the power of *words* and the responsibility we have to use them carefully. Not only are words important but our character also connects to our words."

"Be your words, Shinhon, choose them wisely," the Master said "and you will always be a light to others."

I could not sleep all that night and pondered over the words that were soaring through my head like shooting stars. The Wisdom of Words is a powerful and empowering phenomenon for everyone. Words must be used sparingly, with kindness and responsibility. Not only are our words important, but also the inner character that connects with our words.

"Be your words, Shinhon and choose them wisely, and you will always be a Light to others." the Master said to me.

As I lay awake thinking about this wisdom, it occurred to me that I was getting close to the end of my apprenticeship with the Master. I pondered over what I would do once I had learned the Eight Wisdoms? Where will I go? Soon, I fell asleep with thoughts of the day lingering.

WISDOM 7

"Being unwanted, unloved, uncared for, forgotten by everybody, I think that is a much greater hunger, a much greater poverty than the person who has nothing to eat."

MOTHER TERESA

Search the Impact
of a Life

I was awakened by a servant early the next morning. He held sweet tea and bread in one hand and my clothing for the day in the other.

"Shinhon, good morning, I trust you slept well?" The servant did not appear to expect an answer. He opened the massive curtains for me. "The Master awaits you when you are ready. Call for me or any of the staff if there is anything you need." He bowed and turned away eager to get to his daily chores.

I ate the bread, drank the delicious tea, and dressed for the day. In a few minutes, I was at the Master's door.

"Shinhon," the Master said, "you have performed well as I expected. You have conquered six of the Eight Wisdoms. You have been, and are an excellent apprentice. The last two wisdoms are the keys that unite all you have learned. For the next wisdom you are to go and visit those that you have touched from your other journeys. You should spend time with them and observe how their lives have changed. Enjoy visiting those with whom you have interacted over the years. You will be surprised to see how you have affected their lives, and how your life has been affected by them. Let the spirit be with you and let it guide you."

I was excited to begin the next quest and was warmed by his words.

He spoke again, "Shinhon, there is someone here who wishes to see you before you go."

From around a corner in the great hall I saw the outline of a woman and I recognized her at once, even though it had been many years since that night I had fallen by the campfire before her. I could never forget her. She had saved my life.

"Lelolien," I said.

Her maturity, her kindness, and the love and beauty of her wisdom emanated from her presence. She was just as I remembered. There was never a stronger woman. She shined with a glow of the spirit. Her striking hair was white as snow and flowed down her back, almost touching the middle of her legs, giving her the appearance of an angel. She wore a gown of soft purple material curving around her body.

She came to me with outstretched arms. "Shinhon," she whispered. We embraced as I thought back to the time that this sweet woman nursed me back to health and comforted me when I felt I could not be comforted. That was the absolute worst time in my life when I was nearly dead from grief.

"It is so good to see you my boy," she said. "But look at you," she stepped back, "You are hardly a boy anymore. I have heard so much about your heroic life since we last met. I knew you were special. Even through the excessive pain you felt, your spirit spoke to me and I could see the greatness in you."

"Lelolien, I am grateful that I was led to your campfire. I would have died that night if I had not found you." We both embraced again and smiled at each other. This was a profound reunion between seeker and apprentice.

The Master broke the silence and as we parted he said. "Lelolien, my friend, you have done well in choosing Shinhon as my apprentice. He is an excellent student. He has only two more wisdoms to master, but as you know, Seeker, the last two can be the most difficult."

I thought, 'How could that be?' Lelolien looked at me with loving eyes and said. "You see Shinhon; you are not the only apprentice I have sent to the Master. There were many before you and they all chose a different path than the Masters."

I was surprised to hear that there were others who had failed, but then I remembered how many times I had been tempted to give up.

Lelolien smiled as she said, "Shinhon go and see the people whose lives you have influenced, but please come back to the Master. You may be tempted to stay, but you must come back and finish the final wisdom. Know that the last wisdom may be the hardest test of your young life. Only one person made it to the last wisdom and failed with grave consequences."

"I will come back." I replied.

"See that you do, Shinhon," the Master said. "Now, please go and make ready for your journey. I give you the freedom to do what you will. You may take as long as you wish, but the longer you are away, the more you may forget about the path back to me. Know that if you do not come back you may still enjoy a wonderful life. It is your choice to stay any place that you desire. However, if you come back, as I hope and believe you will, you are to complete your apprentice training, which is the final wisdom."

I thought about the last wisdom and questioned the Master. "After the wisdoms are completed, what happens next? The apprenticeship has been the main focus in my life."

The Master smiled at me. "I remember a boy a few years ago who asked me the question: 'Why does life have to be so hard, and often unfair?'" The Master looked at me and raised his eyebrows while slightly bowing his head. "Shinhon, those who live life can succeed if they choose, but the people who love life are the ones who become real masters. You could leave the palace, never completing the last wisdom, but then you would never realize what could have been."

The Master reached into his clothing and pulled out a parchment. "This is a map of my kingdom and you will have the freedom to visit all the towns and cities that you wish."

"Thank you, Master," I said, "I will return to finish the last wisdom."

I gave Lelolien one last good-bye with a strong embrace and left for my room to get ready for the journey ahead.

As I passed Mehi in the halls I gave her an embrace, telling her that I was leaving for another journey. She said it was nice having me in the palace all this time and she wished me well and told me to please come back.

I went to the room that had been my home for the past year. I thought about where I should go first as there had been a treasure of good memories in each place. I thought about all the things I had learned and the people I had met along the way. A picture formed in my mind of the great merchant, Master Chinsha and his sweet daughter, Aryia, whom I knew was all grown up and would probably be married and have children. My heart ached to see them. Maybe that is where I should go first. The city of Hiin was very close to the palace. I wished many times that I had visited them earlier. I would love to see how Aryia had grown as a young woman. She was a wise soul beyond her years. I touched the amulet around my neck, gazing at it with fond memories of my time with Aryia and Chinsha. I also remembered the times that were not so tender, working in the human and animal waste.

To the Sea

I found the old bag I had carried with me in my travels. I knew it was past time to get a new one. I was able to find a much nicer backpack and, as I transferred my belongings, I found a small piece of parchment crumpled up in one corner of the bag.

The parchment read:

"Thank you so much, Shinhon, I will always remember your kindness. Please visit me if you are ever in Bahe. I wish to attempt to repay you for your kindness to me." It was signed, "Colayin in the city of Bahe."

I remembered this note. Chinsha had given me a task to sell dirt for one hundred pieces of gold. I reminisced about the miracle required to find someone to purchase dirt! I thought it was a joke and so did most of the villagers. I thought back to the time the man begged me to sell the dirt to him. All he had was ten pieces of gold so I made up the difference from my own money. That grateful person was the man named Colayin.

Colayin wanted me to come see him. I looked up the city of Bahe on the map that the Master had given me. Yes, there it was on the far south side of the Master's lands. It had to be my destiny to see this man first. I wondered if the dirt had really aided his wife. He has probably forgotten the boy who sold it to him. I consulted with the Master one last time, bid him farewell, gathered provisions I would need for my long journey, and set forth.

I was on the road again, but this time it was different. I felt light and free. I was not in any hurry to be or do anything. I took time to remember others.

I felt excited to meet all those who had crossed my path before.

I loved the lands south of the Master's holdings. They were so green and the trees were huge. Bahe was a port city. Thinking of it brought back memories of a time in my young life when I had visited the sea with my family. I remembered how beautiful it was.

By now I enjoyed traveling. It was always easy to be close to the Spirit as I enjoyed the beauty of the world. Many nights I wandered into someone's campsite and they always offered me food or drink and a place by the fire to spend the night. I would do the same when a weary traveler came to my campfire.

I had been traveling many days and was beginning to feel weary and hungry when I noticed a brightly lit fire in the distance. The incredible scent of food and the warmth of the fire made me realize how tired and hungry I was. I reached the camp and saw a young man eating a dinner of fowl and beans.

"Hello, fellow traveler," I said.

"Hello," he replied. I stared at his dinner, afraid I would drool if I opened my mouth, but I did not have to worry. He bid me sit down and dine with him. He introduced himself as Shemon from the city of Bahe.

As I ate, or devoured, the beans and meat, I asked the traveler what his business was, so far to the south.

He explained that he had been doing business for the ruler of the city of Bahe. The city of Ivicas supplied much of his city's grain and beans. Now that Ivicas had water reservoirs there was more to harvest and it had become one of the wealthiest cities in the land.

"How are Shim, Shem, and Shom," I asked?

Shim and Shem still lead the town as they always did, but their brother Shom passed away late last year.

I was surprised and saddened to hear this news. Shom was an incredibly wise man for whom I had developed strong feelings.

The man recognized my sadness and asked if I knew them well.

"Yes," I said, "I spent time with all of them some time ago and assisted them with the building of the waterways feeding their land from the Momotha River.

After I mentioned the waterways, the man's eyes grew very big and a look of wonder showed on his face as recognition came to him.

"Are you Shinhon?" he asked.

"Yes I am," I said. "It appears that my name is familiar to you."

He dropped his food in astonishment.

"Oh yes, I have heard of the great Master Shinhon. I thought that you were simply a myth or legend. I have heard so many stories about you and I know that the city of Bahe holds you in high esteem next to the Great Spirit."

"Why does the city hold me in such high respect?" I asked as curiosity overwhelmed me.

The young traveler explained, "The story of our leader and king, Colayin, is well known. He is the reason our city became so prosperous. Because of Colayin's connection to the cities west of the sea, Bahe had become wealthy and prosperous. The city of Bahe has developed into a great port through trade with other countries and communities.

"Several years ago, Colayin was chosen to rule over the city — those were desperate times for our people. The city was in ruins from an unscrupulous leader. Colayin voyaged by sea, traveling in search of a way to help his people. He spoke to many leaders of other countries to encourage trade, loans, and anything possible to rebuild the country. He never grew tired and was determined to find a way to save his people.

"Colayin's journeys took him to a strong, prosperous empire in the west. While there, he had an audience with King Ranex and knew he would be a great ally. The king and Colayin met with the king's counselors to discuss business and how the port city of Bahe could become a great trading power. It was well known that this would benefit both kingdoms.

"Colayin remained in the city many days and was escorted by the king's daughter, the Lady Fena. He found her intelligent and knowledgeable on many subjects. It was not long before Colayin fell madly in love with the beautiful princess, and she with him. Colayin revealed his feelings to her father after she proclaimed her love for him. The king had suspected all along that they were a great match and gave them his blessing. They were married in a regal ceremony. King Ranex was thrilled knowing that with the marriage alliance his country would connect with the Master's territory.

"Colayin came home to Bahe with his beautiful wife, Queen Fena. Soon the land showed signs of prosperity and development through trade.

"The joy of King Colayin turned to grief when Queen Fena became ill. The court physicians feared she would die. Colayin was distraught at the thought of losing his beloved, as her symptoms worsened. One healer said he had observed this form of illness, although it was rare. The healer knew there was a slight chance of a cure for the queen. He spoke of a special kind of soil from a mountainside far away. He explained to the king that his only option would be to travel to the city of Hiin and procure healing dirt from the Helain Mountain. Colayin accepted the task and returned with the miraculous remedy for his queen. She grew stronger each day and was soon well. Our city continued to prosper."

I listened with great interest to Shemon's account of the downfall and growing success of Bahe.

Shemon continued, "Colayin talked about the boy, Shinhon, who would always be honored in the city. There are shrines where we give homage to Shinhon. Stories of him became legends all over the land."

I was stunned. Shrines? Legends? For selling a bucket of dirt to a person in need? I could not believe my ears and thought there must be a mistake.

"I cannot believe I am here, now, with the great Shinhon," he said.

Bewildered, I replied, "I am just a man like any other."

Shemon said, "I will run to the city tomorrow and tell them of your journey to Bahe. You must get a proper welcome from the city. Everyone will rejoice upon your arrival."

We talked and I explained that I followed the Spirit and was just like him. I was learning and growing from the great wisdoms of life. I explained the wisdoms to him. He listened to every word.

Morning came and Shemon was gone. He must have awakened early and left for the city. But, before he left, he had prepared a small meal for me.

I traveled two more days before arriving at the city. It was beautiful, overlooking the boundless ocean.

Coming Home

I approached the main entrance to the city. I thought the gates would be imposing and well-guarded, like those in other cities I had seen, but Bahe was different. A huge gathering of people stood outside. It appeared as though the entire city was there to greet me.

All the people stood in silence and awe as I approached. I did not understand their reaction to me. I was just a kid with some dirt who felt compassion for someone in need.

In front of the massive gathering was a distinguished man. He was dressed in fine apparel with curly flowing locks of hair, pulled back by the crown on his head. I felt a sign of recognition. It was Colayin, the man who begged me for the bucket of sand I thought was useless dirt.

"Shinhon!" he yelled to me. He came to me and wrapped his arms around my shoulders. "I knew you would come someday," he said with a smile. "Please meet my wife, Queen Fena." We bowed at the same time.

"I am so pleased to meet you, Shinhon," she said.

I had never seen a woman like her. She was breathtaking with golden hair and bright blue eyes. I felt her radiating sweetness. I knew instantly that her beauty was also part of her spirit.

Colayin interrupted my thoughts saying that it was time to gather into the city. The silence exploded with shouts from the people. The city was in the midst of a celebration.

I asked Colayin if this was a special day and what the celebration was for.

He smiled, "You, of course, I have prepared for the time that you would visit our land and how we could repay you for the kindness to us many years ago."

"Shemon is the boy you met on the road who ran many miles to tell us of your arrival. Please come to the city square where the people of Bahe have a feast ready for you."

In the square crowds exploded with shouts of joy. People reached out to touch my hand. Everyone seemed electrified.

It was a great celebration, including all kinds of food and a variety of entertainers — fire breathers, beautiful dancers, and storytellers recited tales of my adventures, Some I remembered and others I knew has never happened to me. I laughed at them. They made me sound so heroic. I never thought of myself in such a glorious light.

The celebration went well into the night. Colayin and Fena were gracious. The city was alive with good will. After the celebration, Colayin showed me around the huge palace. I had never seen a more grandiose building in all my travels. The Master's palace might be bigger, but certainly not more elegant.

Colayin told me that the palace was built after the city became prosperous due to trading with lands to the west and south of the sea.

I was then escorted to my room and astonished by its splendor. Colayin explained the room was built for me, knowing that someday I would come to his city. The walls were made of gold laminate design and there were sculptures from different parts of the world all over the room. Silk tapestries, embroidered and woven in bright colors, hung from the high ceiling. Two large windows of colored glass adorned the wall along with a small picture window overlooking the sea. The bed appeared to be made of gold with intricate bent bar designs.

"This is much too generous, I exclaimed. All I did was sell you some dirt that was not even mine. I sold it for the merchant Chinsha, as a task given to me. He should have been given this honor."

I did not know what else to say.

"I have followed your adventures since learning of the battle to the north with the Tundins," Colayin said. "Every time I heard news of you, both the city and I rejoiced in your victories. You are a special

217

man, Shinhon. I knew it the moment I met you when you were a boy in the city of Hiin. I am at your command; anything you wish is yours because I owe all this to you."

I felt that he put too much emphasis on what I had done. Somehow I had been made a hero but I knew I was only a man who did my best to live my life with honor and dignity.

Curious to see where it led, I opened a bright purple door at the far end of the room. It revealed a balcony overlooking the sea. I was captivated by its beauty. Even in the night, with a full moon I could see the wonder and magnificence of the world of Bahe.

I reminisced about Shom, one of the brothers who ruled Ivicas, who had passed away. I thought of the Wisdom of Gratitude that Shom taught me and of all the good things his life stood for. Looking out over the beautiful ocean I was overwhelmed with gratitude and love for the people who honored me.

The next morning I awoke and was privileged to eat breakfast with Colayin and Fena. Breakfast was served in a great hall where young children screamed and played with each other. I was introduced to the king's children — three bright eyed little boys full of life and energy.

"This is my oldest" the king told me. "His name is Shinhon. He was a miracle to us since Fena gave birth to him after being healed from the illness she experienced. We named him after you to honor and remember you."

I am honored indeed. "Thank you," I said.

"So, how are you Shinhon?" I asked the young boy.

"I am very good," he said. "It is a pleasure to meet you."

The oldest child studied me, while he shoved a piece of bread in his mouth. "We have heard so much of your travels. Sometimes I feel it is hard to have your name. It is a name that I must live up to." He chewed on his food, not willing to give up eating for our dialogue.

I smiled. "I am sure you will honor your name in your own way, with your own life."

He smiled back at me.

After breakfast I was shown around the city, and saw the huge port with the ships that sailed to lands far away. It was obvious the people loved Colayin. He was a just and kind ruler. The energy of the city was that of love and prosperity. I felt more at home here than at any place in all my travels, even the Master's palace.

I assisted Colayin with everything. As I adapted to my new life, I fell in love with Bahe. I knew I could live here forever and be happy. With the passing of time, I thought less of the Master and the Wisdoms, and only focused on the love of this place and the people here. I spent many hours on the balcony of my room in the palace looking out at the beauty of the sea. How content I was! I felt more loved than any man could ever expect. Was the last Wisdom really so important? I had learned so much and the Master himself had said if I did not return to his palace it would be my choice.

I thought maybe it was time to start living my own life. Maybe I should stop trying so hard to please another and just enjoy what I had.

I found myself thinking about the man in the Master's court who had complained about how he tried and tried, yet always failed. I had not failed in my search for the Wisdoms—I was successful and had learned how powerful, we, as individuals can be. I had not been trying but had succeeded and maybe it was time to relax and enjoy the fruit of my labors.

Time went by and life was good. I still adhered to the Wisdoms that were now a great part of me. I ate sparingly, meditated daily, said prayers, and exercised as a warrior. I ran to the cliffs on the beach every day. I looked at the good in my life and was grateful for all I had. I could see the beauty of life. I loved the world.

One day Colayin asked me to visit with him. As we talked he said "Shinhon, Bahe is your home and I wish that you would make it your permanent home. I ask that you make the decision to be my adviser and rule Bahe with me.

I asked how a boy that sold him some healing dirt many years ago, could now stand before him and refuse an offer of this magnitude.

Colayin said, "When I looked into your eyes that day I was so helpless and distraught about my Fena. I would have given anything to make my wife well. I offered you all I had. You had such compassion and goodness in your eyes when you told me that ten pieces of gold was enough. I knew that you were destined to be a great man."

I told him, "I do not know how to reply. You have built this city

up from a village and now you want me to assist you in ruling it. I am
honored and I think you have done well."

"I know that you would contribute much to the growth of Bahe."
Colayin said. "Anyone around you can feel your goodness and your
greatness. You have a light within you that shines."

"Thank you for believing in me. I will give you an answer tomorrow,"
I said.

As I meditated in the garden that morning the Spirit was strong.

"Search deep into your heart, into your deepest feelings, and you
will know what must be done."

I meditated for most of the day and knew there were things I needed
to accomplish before settling in one place. Saddened by this revelation,
I knew for sure that I must leave Bahe and the people I had grown to
love.

I was content here but I also knew, without question, that I had not
yet completed the comprehension of the Wisdom of Relationships and
there were still many people to reconnect with. My desire to complete
all the wisdoms was foremost in my life so I made preparations to leave
the city.

I slept that night and upon awaking in the morning I went to bid
Colayin, Fena, and the children farewell.

I told him of the love I had for him and his family, and the people
of this city, and how grateful I was for everything that had transpired
there.

I was thankful that the dirt he received from me had saved Fena's
life.

I told him it was time for me to go. I must go back to the city of
Ivicas, and visit the brothers, Shim and Shem. I was close to them and
knew I needed to see them next.

I told Colayin that he was a great leader and his people loved him. I
knew he would lead the city in love and goodness. I wished Fena love
and light, and thanked her for her hospitality.

I said goodbye to their children. I told the boy, Shinhon, that he
could grow up to be whoever he wanted to be, no matter what his name
was and felt it a splendid honor to have him as a namesake.

Colayin called a meeting in the city and explained that I would be leaving. I spoke to the gathering, telling the people of my love for them and thanking them for all the love they had shown me. I told them I would miss them and that they would all be in my thoughts and prayers.

I prepared to leave and packed what few things I would need for my journey to the village of Ivicas. I studied the map and was soon on my way.

Friends of Thought

It felt good to run through the lands. I arrived at Ivicas many days later. By now, I had become used to traveling and discovered that I enjoyed it.

Ivicas had grown while I was away. The village was now a thriving city, with people running to and fro. As I got closer, I saw the farms. They were bigger and greener than I remembered. New people must be moving in all the time. There were more inns to stay in than I remembered.

As I walked down the street towards the square, where the brothers held court, a man yelled to me. "Shinhon! Shinhon! Is that you?" A man came running up to me. I looked at him and knew I had never seen this man before though he appeared to know me.

"Shinhon, it is you," he repeated as he grabbed me giving me a strong embrace. He had a smile on his face and laughed as he saw how bewildered I was. I knew I would have remembered someone like him. He was a large man with bulging muscles and looked strong enough to pull up trees.

"Shinhon, it is sad that you do not recognize me," he said with a smile. "You saved my life and changed my pathetic existence. We met past the west desert in the village under the temple."

I searched my memory, looking at the man.

"Peebal," I said with astonishment. "Is that you?"

He laughed and smiled. "Yes," he said "Yes, it is I, Peebal, the sad blob of a man that you met in the village under the temple. I know that I appear much different than when we last met. After we spoke so long ago, I left the village and found farms to work and people who would hire me. There were times that I thought I would die, but I continued working and became stronger and felt better from the hard work I did. I was sought after because of my strength and ability to accomplish so much work. I married a farmer's daughter and became a transformed person. It has been many years, but I would never forget you. Laotzu was inspired to send you to me."

"It is good to see you," I said.

Peebal told me that his heart was filled with gratitude for his life. He now looked at all phases of life through different eyes.

At the mention of gratitude, I felt a slight twinge in my emotions. Shom would have liked this man as he had learned the wisdom of "the attitude of gratitude."

I told him I was going to the court to see my friends, the brothers Shim and Shem. I had learned that Shom, the oldest brother passed away. He told me he was also going there to do business for his village where he was trading for seeds. We walked together into the court square. I remembered it well. It was such a good place and the people were loving and free.

Shim and Shem saw me at once. Shem jumped out of his chair and ran to me, grabbing me in a bear hug, almost taking my breath away. "Shinhon, you have returned. It is so good to see you. We were hoping that you would come back."

They sat back in the comfortable chairs and introduced me to the court. Many cheered as I waved at the people. "Hurray, Shinhon has returned." The towns people were happy to see me. I was humbled because of their love for me.

Shim explained that Shom had passed away.

"Yes," I said, "I heard about his death in my travels. He was a great man."

"Yes," Shim said. "He is missed."

I introduced Peebal to Shim and Shem and told them the story of how we met. Peebal explained his life's journey's to them.

We were invited to Shem's home for dinner after the court. They asked if I would sit in Shom's chair. The city had grown so much since I was last here. Shem explained that since the water ducts were put in place the city had grown exponentially.

The food was magnificent and the conversation, as always, both delightful and enlightening. Peebal enjoyed himself, getting along well with the brothers.

After dinner we all talked on the porch, looking over the great garden, watching the sun disappear. At one point Shim stood up and brought something over to me. He said this is Shom's gratitude journal and he wanted me to have it.

He explained that Shom had written half the book and wanted me to write the rest, explaining my gratitude, adventures, and journey into learning the eight wisdoms and how they had changed my life.

I told him I would always cherish it and write in it often. I explained that I had so much to be grateful for, due to the many relationships I had made on my journeys. With a smile, Shem clapped me rather hard on the back and explained that they were honored to associate with me as well.

We had a good time that night and were given comfortable rooms to sleep in. Peebal explained his business to the brothers and they said they would get the seeds for him.

The next day, we met for breakfast together. At the table the brothers told me they wanted to ask me something. Shim said they had liked the way the three brothers worked together and they needed a third person to govern the city with them. He said, "Shinhon, you know the importance of thought and you love the people. We would like you to stay and govern them with us. Shom's home would be your home."

I thought how wonderful it would be to live in Ivicas and be part of the lives of the brothers and their people, but I also knew that this was impossible because I had made a commitment not only to the Master but to myself. I explained to them that I could not accept their gracious offer, even though I would be honored to govern with them. I was committed to finishing my training.

I felt a flash of insight as I explained my thoughts to the brothers. "You know, Peebal had experiences like you and learned the importance of gratitude. I know him and know that he has a good heart. He would make a just and fair leader. He knows the power of thought well."

The brothers talked for a while and asked Peebal if he would be interested in helping to lead the city. Peebal was humbled and accepted, saying he would need to go back home, get everything in order, and gather his family.

I stayed in Ivicas for some time, enjoying the love of all the people and the brothers, but, at last, I realized it was time for me to leave. I gathered my belongings and searched the map looking for my next destination. It was the great city of Chee to the east. I thought of the baker and the boys he had taken in under his loving care. It had been some time and I was anxious to see them again, so I bid the brothers farewell and left, looking forward to my next adventure.

Friends and Enemies

That night I sat in my camp and read the book of gratitude from Shom. I then took my piece of charcoal and wrote my first entry.

I am grateful for the relationships and friendships I made along the way in my short lifetime. I have been blessed with knowing so many good people. I wrote of my time in Bahe with Colayin's people. I wrote of the joy of meeting once again with Peebal and the brothers. I would always be grateful for the opportunity to meet and get to know Shom, and would never forget him. As I ended my remarks, I wrote that I was writing these words in my Journal of Gratitude.

I awoke bright and early, ready to begin a new day. The campfire from the night before had turned to ashes long before I awoke. I lit the little fire again and added kindling. As I boiled water for my sweet tea, I ate the bread and fruit I had with me. Many thoughts whirled through my mind. I had stayed up most of the night reading and writing in my journal and was anxious to commune with the Great Spirit.

After a hard workout, I gathered my thoughts and peace flowed through my body. I sat down to meditate, feeling empowered after listening to the Spirit. All the bouncing thoughts cleared in my mind. I could pick wisdoms, one by one, to meditate upon. I gathered my provisions and traveled to the city of Chee.

While traveling I thought about the baker, Mitsuo, and the boys Uery and Yer. I was eager to see them again. I was sure Mitsuo would be the wealthiest man in the city because his pastries were irresistible. I had fond memories of helping Mitsuo. He was a kind and loving person and I was grateful to be a part of his life, honored to assist him. My mouth watered, remembering the delicacies.

Eventually, I arrived at the city of Chee and was surprised that there was no activity as I approached. The front gates were heavily guarded, much more so than I remembered. One of the guards stopped me and asked, "What is your business in Chee?"

I said, "Hello," and reached out my hand, but drew it back when he frowned and looked at me fiercely. "I have come to Chee to visit a friend," I offered.

"What friend, stranger?" asked the guard.

"The baker, Mitsuo, and his sons." I explained that they were good friends of mine.

"Mitsuo and his sons are imprisoned in the dungeons and have been there for a long time." He grimaced as he spoke Mitsuo's name.

"Who are you?" the guard asked.

I never knew a kinder or more loving man than Mitsuo. How could he be in prison? My soul felt burdened by this information and the spirit whispered, "Be careful what you say."

"I find it hard to believe," I told the guard. "There must be some mistake or you must mean a different Mitsuo. Why is he imprisoned?"

The guard looked down at me and replied harshly, "For practicing magic." Then he asked in a strict and loud voice, "Who are you and what is your business with Mitsuo?"

I replied, "I am Shinhon, and am well known in this city. I can vouch for Mitsuo as he is a good man."

"Shinhon," the man said with his mouth closed tight, seeming to choke at the sound of my name.

"You are Shinhon, apprentice to the Master?" he questioned me.

"Yes," I replied.

He screamed in a loud voice, "Seize him!" Within seconds iron grips were clasped around my arms.

I yelled, "What is this? I have done nothing."

He ignored me, saying, "We have the great Shinhon. Take him to the emperor at once. He will be pleased."

Two guards rushed me through the city. As we went I noticed how different it was from my memory. The spirit was gone and in its place were dark clouds and sadness. The people appeared fearful and looked down when they saw me, hurrying faster to get to their destination. The bustling city I remembered had turned quiet and sullen.

We passed the market. There were some vendors, but soldiers now controlled their activities. The people were in a state of total despair.

The guard holding me told a guard at the door of the palace, "We have the great Shinhon!" He looked like he had just won a prize. The Emperor, Udoki, will want to see him right away.

A guard opened the huge, golden doors.

'What did he say? Emperor Udoki?'

Visions flashed into my head of a time long ago, a panoramic vision of my family tortured and killed at the hands of raiding evil warlords.

Udoki! My blood boiled. A rage burned within me, hotter than ever. The Wisdoms faded to a distant reflection. The only thought I had left was to kill Udoki.

There were more guards inside. The golden doors led into a great room. There he sat on a throne, looking aged and dark. They took me into the room. The anger I felt made me more vengeful than ever. I had been keeping my body in shape for this moment, I thought. I was strong and agile from my soldier training with Makato. I was a warrior, more than ready for what I needed to do.

I broke free of the soldier's firm grip and, with the speed of lightning, spun my body, reaching down to pull the sword from the hand of another soldier. There was no time for them to react. There were others in the room but all were caught off guard—including the ugly vicious warlord I planned to run the sword through. I was on him before anyone knew what had happened. I would have my revenge. Raising the sword, I looked deep into his terrified eyes. I desperately wanted to watch him die.

I hesitated for an instant, startled, then let the sword fall to my side. "You are not Udoki?" That split second was all the guards needed. They smashed me to the ground with one foot on my neck.

I yelled as I pushed up through the bodies holding me down. "You are not Udoki!"

Overcome with disappointment and exhaustion, I stopped fighting. After what seemed like an eternity, the soldiers brought me to my feet. The emperor looked at me with a smile. "That will not happen again." He motioned to a guard to bring shackles, which were placed on my feet and hands. There was no way to get free.

Who was this rat-faced man? He was not the fierce warlord whose eyes I had looked into as a boy.

"Who are you?" I asked?

"So you knew the Udoki?" He roared with laughter. "He led a massive war party to the east for many years. The mention of his name drew fear and terror throughout the land. He was ruthless. Many years ago he disbanded his terror group and disappeared. He has not been seen for many years, but his name lives on. I took the name to intensify respect. My group has become bigger and more superior throughout the years. We moved west with a mission to seize the Master's land. The city of Chee is the first of many we intend to control. It is firmly in my hegemony as the city of Bahe soon will be. The port will secure our dominance on the south side of the Master's lands. After securing these borderlands, we will dominate the west. Taking you prisoner is an unexpected bonus. I will have you executed in the morning in the town square. This will send a bold message to the people. The great Shinhon, killed by Udoki. Nothing will stop me from my conquests."

My energy was spent, my life force drained. I thought of my family and felt defeated. I almost missed the false Udoki's talk of the city he planned to conquer next. My heart leaped as I realized he was speaking about the good people of Bahe whom I loved. I was not afraid to die, however, I felt I still had much to accomplish. The Master! It was difficult to imagine not seeing him again. Was it possible he did not know what was happening?

Udoki, the imposter, spoke. "I want triple the soldiers tomorrow on hand for the execution. I do not want the death of the great Shinhon starting a riot.

"You were friends with the baker, Mitsuo. I will allow you to spend your last night with him in the dungeon. Mitsuo and his sons were much too powerful for me to allow them to be free. His baked goods were so delicious they infected the entire town. It was obvious he used magic to create such delicacies. He and his sons will rot in the dungeons."

The evil man crinkled his ugly face and roared with laughter. I thought, not only did he look like a rat, his laughter was also rat-like. My senses were returning and I knew I wanted to stop this man, impossible as it seemed. I reprimanded myself for not taking him when I had the chance.

"Take the great Shinhon away," he said with a sarcastic snicker, "and lock him up with the baker. Send an announcement out to the city that there will be an execution tomorrow. This will begin the supremacy of my power. It will prove to these people that I am more powerful than the great Master by destroying his number one servant.

The guards took me away. I struggled in their grip but the struggle was senseless.

They dragged me out of the palace and into the depths of the city where the acrid smell of death and disease was strong. I had never seen such hopelessness, not even in the leper city to the north. We approached a door filthy with rust. It creaked open; I was shoved inside; the latch was locked behind me. Dim light came through the bars from lanterns in the hallway.

Looking around, I saw three men peering at me like shadows. One spoke, "Who is the poor unfortunate man who shares our fate, rotting in this pit of hell? "

I recognized his voice. It was Mitsuo, the baker who was once a beggar.

"Mitsuo," I whispered, "It is your friend, Shinhon."

"Shinhon!!" They yelled in unison, running to me in astonishment, scrutinizing me, hoping it wasn't really me.

"Shinhon, my friend," Uery cried. He hugged me, so much bigger, no longer just a boy. I knew he had been here quite a while. He stank like the air, — or lack of it — in our prison cell.

"All is lost." said Mitsuo, "if you are here with us."

I told him not for long because I would be executed in the morning.

"Better to die tomorrow then rot down here." Uery said.

From what they could remember, they had been imprisoned for many months, though they insisted they were glad to be together as father and sons. They were all painfully thin and admitted to eating the rotten bread rations and sometimes catching rats. No one could live in this hellhole for long. I thought.

We spent the night talking about the past. They explained how the old emperor of the city had been pleased with them. The city had grown, thanks to the great man, but the evil warlord, Udoki, had brutally slaughtered him.

I shouted, "That man is not Udoki. He is an imposter, but the real Udoki would be worse." They did not know the difference.

They talked about how they had grown wealthy and respected in the city. It was a good life. Then the raiders came and took over the city before anyone knew what was happening. The emperor was killed and Udoki declared the city his.

Mitsuo explained that the leader, Udoki, seeing the respect we had, thought us a threat, declared us sorcerers. He said the food that we made could not be normal food, only magical. He then locked us in this dungeon to rot.

Then Yer spoke, "Master Shinhon, you are great and powerful. Will you be able to change this terrible situation?" I looked at him saying, "I do not know what to do or how I can be of any assistance." His look of despair cut me to the quick.

Uery spoke again, "Almost no one who comes to the city is allowed to enter, and none to leave. I do not think anyone knows our fate."

"I wouldn't be too sure. The Master is wiser than us all, though it may be too late for me," I said.

The night passed and it was good to be with friends. Soon the guards came and opened the door to the cell. "Come great Shinhon. We are letting you go free, but you must never come back to Chee." I was shocked. "You are freeing me?" I looked at one of the guards and saw that he had a wicked smirk on his face. They both broke into laughter.

"No, Shinhon, this is your day to die."

A Day to Die

The guards grabbed me and rushed me through the dungeon. Soon we were out in the light of day. My movement was slow as I was still shackled. Many spectators wept aloud in grief. I knew they were thinking all was lost. The slow journey to my death was painful. The despair I felt for the people crushed my soul.

I was led to a platform in the middle of the square. In the center of the platform was a cradle for my head. On the stage stood one giant man, a hood covered his face, and in his hand was a massive ax waiting to lop off my head.

I stumbled as I climbed to the platform. My heart was pounding — as if it were trying to spend all its allotted beats as quickly as it could. My life passed before me as I thought of all the things I would not be able to accomplish and how much more there was to do. My knees grew weak.

All that I had learned and accomplished was wasted. I had sworn I would come back to the Master and finish the last Wisdom. And now this is how I would end. Step by step the two soldiers let me on toward the man with the ax. At least it would be quick.

At last I stood before the executioner on the platform. The soldiers pushed me down on my knees in front of the block. In only a few moments my head would be separated from my body.

As the terrible ax was raised over my head, I could see, in the corner of my eye that something was happening in the crowd. Many of the people in tattered clothing started to remove their garments and underneath their clothing was soldier's armor. What was this? I turned my head slightly to look at the giant man and the axe that was seconds from coming down on me. He was massive and I wondered if I had ever seen a man that big? He swung the ax but as it plummeted down toward my head, it turned, and in one swoop penetrated both the soldiers. They lay dead without ever knowing what had happened. I was in a daze, not comprehending. A loud bellow came from the executioner.

"On to Victory!" It sounded like thunder. He swept off the hood and garment that covered him.

I looked at the massive man, General Yosha. A smile came to the man's face as his eyes met mine.

He commanded me to put my shackled hands on the block. Yosha raised the axe again. With a quick chop my hands were separated from the chains. Another quick hack to the bonds on my feet set me free.

From behind him the general grabbed a sword and handed it to me. "We fight as brothers," he said simply. The men who had dropped their rags were fighting soldiers caught off guard in the chaos.

Yosha yelled, "People of the city of Chee, fight for your freedom, fight for your lives."

People picked up anything they could use against the enemy. In desperation and rage, they fought for their lives. The gloom that had covered the people and the entire city lifted with their passion.

Yosha yelled to me that his men were now opening the gate and, as we fought, his army would catch the guards by surprise. Soldiers tried to attack us but were cut down. We jumped into the middle of the fight. Adrenalin flowed. The doors were opened and a rush of men flooded the city. I had provided the perfect diversion for Yosha's army.

We fought hard; any soldiers foolish enough to fight Yosha were taken down quickly.

I still felt vengeance in my heart as I looked for the emperor to find out more about the real Udoki.

Soon the army surrendered and was rounded up. The fake Udoki, the one called "emperor" was one of the casualties. I only wished I could have gotten to him first.

I asked some of the surviving men about the real Udoki, but they were no help.

The city was free and the people were excited. Yosha started to rebuild governing order immediately and gathered as many of the leaders as he could. He told the people in the city that a court would convene to rebuild.

I grabbed the great man's arm. "Thank you. I was sure I was going to meet the Great Spirit today."

He smiled and put his hand on my shoulder. "It was perfect. I had kept my army to the north waiting for the right opportunity. We wanted to minimize damage to the city itself. We had found a way to sneak a few men inside and knew that if we could storm the city with the gates open it would be easy. When our spy came to me last night and told me of your capture and your scheduled execution, I knew it was the perfect opportunity. I had heard of your travels. I knew you were special. Even now, if not for you, I would still be wondering how to take back the city. I am happy to see you again, Master Shinhon. You have grown into a great man."

I put my arm on the general's shoulder and said, "I need to release some people from the dungeons." I took some men and in the depths freed many men and women, leaders and merchants.

I came to Mitsuo's rusted door. It was opened. "Mitsuo, Uery, and Yer, you are now free." They rose up from the floor.

"Who is that?" Uery said. They looked and Mitsuo said, "Shinhon! How can this be?"

I told them of my rescue and how General Yosha had taken back the city. They were too weak to jump for joy, but thrilled at the outcome.

We left the dungeons. It took them some time to get used to the light but I noticed that Mitsuo was walking normally. When I first found him he was a beggar because he had been crippled at birth.

"How is it you walk so well?" I asked.

He smiled and lifted up his leg. "I had this special shoe made," he explained. It leveled his foot, rendering his limp unnoticeable.

The old and just emperor had been killed by the enemy, so Yosha asked if there was anyone strong enough to lead. He called for a vote of the people to select the next emperor.

I stood in the court, raising my hands so I could speak. "I have been in Chee before and love this city. I do suggest someone that I would put to the vote. As you all know, Mitsuo, the baker, is a good man and I believe he would lead this city fairly and just. I ask that you consider this man. He was a great support to the last emperor and he knows the city well."

There was murmur and talk. A wave of communication went through the massive crowd. Yosha raised his arms for attention and stood before the city. "We all know of the greatness of Shinhon. I respect his judgment above all others." There were cheers of agreement. "Who would vote that Mitsuo, the baker, should be emperor to this city?"

A huge roar ensued, strong and hard.

Yosha raised his arms again to quiet the crowd. Still they yelled with great excitement. "Is there anyone against?" Some raised their hands but few compared to those in favor. "It is now decided that the new emperor will be Mitsuo."

I had no doubts that the city would be in good hands. I knew this loving man well and I was aware of his intelligence. He would lead this city and the people would have a just and fair leader.

We stayed in Chee for many days as governance resumed and trade was reestablished. Many traders had been kept from returning to their homes.

Mitsuo assisted in restructuring the city. He regained his strength and showed great leadership.

Yosha, Mitsuo and I talked long into the nights. I loved being with Yosha again and spent much more time with him than I had in the past. He was as I remembered him, a master leader.

Soon I felt that it was time for me to leave. I knew that all would be well. Yosha left to find the rest of the enemy soldiers scattered around the land disbanded and unable to regroup.

I got out my map to see where I should go next. I felt that I had learned much about this wisdom. Relationships in this world are everything. How terrible it would be to have no one. The hermits in the world must be miserable.

I looked at the map and knew there was one more place that I should visit. It was the city of Hiin. I wanted to see the merchant, Chinsha and his sweet daughter Aryia, if she had not married someone and gone to a distant land.

The Last Relationship

I said my farewells, bid the great general goodbye, and wished the new leader love and light. I had traveled all over the Master's land and was excited to see the merchant, Chinsha.

It took a long time to get to the great city. I passed right by the Master's palace on the way. I did not stop because I wanted to finish my tasks before I returned.

I had forgotten how massive this city was. It was filled with all kinds of people. I passed through the market remembering the time I spent there selling dirt. I thought about how that one act had changed the fate of the city of Bahe.

It had been many years, but I remembered exactly where Chinsha's home was. It awakened good memories and some not so good. I glanced at one of the entrances to the sewers.

Soon, I found myself close to Chinsha's home. Many people were in the streets. In front of his home, I saw a woman talking to a decrepit female street merchant. Even from this distance I could tell that the woman speaking was a beautiful young woman. I walked closer and heard her laughter as she spoke. It sounded like sweet summer wind chimes.

I was close now, maybe twenty steps from them. I stopped and stared. The young woman looked up and her eyes met mine. Her brow furrowed in a question, then opened in recognition as she yelled, "Shinhon!" She left the merchant and ran about to me. "Shinhon," she yelled again.

Standing in front of me was the most beautiful woman I had ever seen, yelling my name. In my mind I thought that I had never seen her before. Not this woman. Her arms were around me in a flash. Tears streamed down her cheeks. She felt resilient but not powerfully strong. She pulled back for a second and I was lost in the dark deepness of her eyes. Who was this beautiful woman?

With that thought she read my mind.

She said in a higher pitch, "You do not know who I am, do you?" I felt the tone of disappointment heavy in my heart.

"Yes, it has been some time," she said, "still, I could never forget you."

She put her hand up to me and touched the necklace I had received so many years ago from the sweet daughter of the merchant.

"You still wear my necklace," she said, "but you do not remember me."

"Aryia," I said in astonishment.

"I cannot believe you have forgotten me so easily." She was very upset, wiping tears from her eyes and her face.

"Sweet Aryia," I choked out. "How could I possibly have recognized you? I remembered you as a sweet child, but now, you are the most beautiful woman I have ever seen."

The directness of my words softened her demeanor and I sensed that she felt a little awkward. Once again she wiped her tears away and exclaimed that she was glad to see me alive and well. "Your name is known throughout the land. I always knew you were someone special."

"As I did you," I said.

"I am deeply hurt, Shinhon, and sweet words will not heal me that quickly."

As I stared at her I could see the resemblance. The outlines of the sweet girl I remembered. But now, my heart ached as I looked at her. I had never felt this way about anyone.

"Is your father well," I asked?

"Oh yes, he is old, but busy as always. I have assisted him as much as possible."

I looked at her and said, "As beautiful as you are you must have a husband by now."

She blushed and laughed uneasily. "No, I am not married."

You must have someone who desires you.

"Oh yes," she said, "many, but I am still waiting for the right one."

What a lucky man he would be, I thought. My heart ached as I looked at her.

"Come," she said. "Let's find my father. He will be happy to see you." She led me to the familiar house.

It looked to me like her feet did not touch the floor. She moved so effortlessly. I don't remember ever looking at someone like this, or even caring how another walked. What had come over me? At that moment I realized I never wanted to be away from this person. The thought of her not being a part of my life was physically painful.

How can this be? I have only seen her for a few minutes and when I saw her last she was just a child. How could I immediately be so madly and passionately in love with this woman? I was stupefied, and excited by her beauty.

She asked a servant, "Where is my father? We have a guest. Shinhon has come to see us."

The servant turned to me and said, "Oh, welcome, Master Shinhon. He is in the study."

"Thank you," I replied.

We went into the study and there sat the merchant, just as I remembered him. His eyes twinkled. "Shinhon," he said, "you have grown up — you are no longer a boy."

"Yes," I said. "It is good to see you, Master Chinsha. In my eyes you have not changed at all."

"I walk a little slower these days," he said with a smile. "Come and eat with us in the dining room. We will get you a room and make you comfortable. Aryia, show Shinhon to the main guest suite."

She took my hand and we walked. Her soft touch sent a wave of warmth through my body. She did not talk to me and I knew that she must still be angry.

She said, "This is your quarters. Get some rest and I will come for you later."

I said, "Yes, sweet Aryia, and thank you."

She stuck up her nose at my words and said, "I will be back."

I could not take my eyes off her. When she disappeared around a corner, my body ached just knowing she was away from me. All I could think about was when she would come back.

I got comfortable in the room and rested but I did not sleep. . . I thought only of Aryia. Why was I so overwhelmed by her? I did not know. I only knew that I wanted her with me.

The hours passed as I thought of what I had learned to get to this point. I thought of relationships and the importance of the people. I was grateful for the many who had crossed my path and assisted me in learning. I said a prayer to the Great Spirit giving thanks for my life and what I had produced. Life is what you make it and the people you meet along the way assist in sculpting the life you create.

It was some time before I heard a knock on the door. "Dinner," she said. I jumped and was at the door in a moment but when I opened it Aryia was already down the hall.

After some wrong turns, I remembered how to get to the dining area. There sat Chinsha and beside him Aryia. Her big dark eyes looked at me with indifference.

I was asked to sit down. We ate and talked for a long time.

The merchant spoke, "I have heard much of your life, Shinhon. You have made quite a name for yourself. Aryia was always the first to tell me the news about you and always first to know of your adventures."

"Yes," she said. "Some of us remember our friends."

Chinsha smiled and spoke, "Aryia told me you did not remember her."

"I asked for her forgiveness. It has been a long time since I last saw her and she has grown into a very beautiful woman; so beautiful that I did not recognize her at first."

Her piercing eyes showed disgust as she said, "You expected me barefoot, fat, and pregnant. Sorry to disappoint you."

Chinsha spoke once again, "She has had many suitors but always pushed them away. I have told her that she will end up alone."

"I am fine taking care of you, father," she said.

"I will not always be here, my child," was his reply.

We continued to talk about my time away and what I had learned. They talked about their experiences as well. It was an enjoyable dinner.

Chinsha said, "You should explore the city. Much has changed since you were last here. The tower with the clock still works but the city has grown. Aryia, please escort Shinhon through the city and let him see the changes for himself."

"I would like that very much," I said. She replied, "I have so much to do, but I could take you for a short walk." After dinner we left for a tour of the city.

Aryia and I stood in front of the merchant's home as the sun was starting to set. The man who managed the lanterns on the street began to light them for the night. We went to the market and the merchants were taking down their canvas tents, packing their wares upon completion of another day. The city had grown so much in the time I was away.

Aryia walked just a few steps in front of me. I found it difficult to look at the city since all I could or wanted to see was her. I could smell her sweetness, the scent of a woman. I wanted to bury my face in her hair. We talked very little. As the sun began to disappear I could no longer restrain myself. I reached for her arm and turned toward her. Her eyes glittered amidst the sparks of the lanterns.

"Aryia, please forgive me. You must understand that the second I saw you in front of your home, I was mesmerized by you. I have never looked at anyone else this way. I have met so many in my travels, but have never felt that I could not live without someone. I feel that way about you."

I whispered the words, "I love you with all my heart, Aryia." Tears ran down her face as she whispered back to me in her angelic voice. "I have always loved you, Shinhon. There has never been anyone but you."

I wrapped myself around her waist, holding her as if I could never let go. I felt a bond so strong I wanted to melt into her. I heard her whisper, "Please, Shinhon, never leave me again."

We held each other and paused only long enough so I could look into her eyes again. Then, softly and slowly, our lips touched in a long tender kiss.

We walked down the street arm in arm, not talking, but feeling the love we shared.

Stay or Go

It took only one day for her to become the center of my existence. Only for an instant did I think of the last wisdom the Master would have for me. The thought was instantaneous and brief.

I spent many days at the merchant's house and every second I could with Aryia. I had never been more content or happy. We talked of our life together and what we wanted to do.

One day, as we ate our lunch on a hill near the city, Aryia asked me, "Are you finished being apprentice to the Master?" I paused for just a moment. "The Master does have one more wisdom for me. I am supposed to go back one last time. I have been thinking whether or not I should. Maybe I should just stay and live the rest of my life with you."

With a questioning glance she looked at me, "Yes, Shinhon. You have been through more difficult times than most. Many times you could have been killed.

I thought of the last wisdom and the promise I had made to myself and the Master.

Days passed and we talked of marriage. Chinsha was happy when we told him and he gave us his blessing.

One night I had a dream. I stood in a merchant shop. The merchant was a man with no face and on the counter lay seven pieces of gold. The man behind the counter said through his empty face. "This is not enough. You have learned seven. The price was eight."

I felt myself saying in my dream. "Seven is all I have."

"Then you cannot have it," the blank-faced man said.

I woke up in a sweat to a new day.

I didn't need an interpreter for the dream. I knew what it meant. To live the best life I could I must learn the last Wisdom. I told Aryia of the dream, concluding, "I love you with all my heart and never want to be away from you, but I must finish the wisdoms with the Master. I agreed to learn the last wisdom, but I will be back and we will be married. I promise."

"I am frightened I will never see you again," she cried. I promised her I would return. Once again, I prepared to leave and said my farewells. I left my love standing there, tears in her eyes. My heart felt empty. My future was Aryia, and I knew that. I was anxious to finish the wisdoms.

Relationships: The Wisdom of Connections

The familiar palace came into view. I was here once again. Many times before when I was excited as the palace came into view I felt as though I was home, but not today. There was a deep foreboding in my heart. I did not want to know...the last wisdom. I only wanted to go back to Aryia, and begin our life together.

I had learned so much about life and could see how good and wonderful it could be. What more could there be that was so important? I entered the palace gates. I was anxious to find the Master, but was informed he was gone and would return later. I was welcomed by everyone and was treated with great respect. I loved the people in the palace, but wanted to get started as soon as possible in hopes that this would not be a wisdom that would take me years to finish.

I walked through the palace. I made it to the great garden were I planned to meditate. There, hard at work in the garden, was an ancient old man.

"Old man Chu!" I yelled. He looked up with an antique face and I thought that there might have been a smile under the lack of expression. "Old man Chu" I said again.

"Hey boy" he replied, in a tone that was kind of like "please pass the water."

"What are you doing here?" I asked. "It has been so many years, I thought, and paused for a moment.

Old man Chu answered before I could finish with, "Yes, I suppose you thought I would be on this earth no more. I am old, but still useful." he said, as he motioned his eyes around the garden.

"Why are you not at the farm?" I queried.

"The farm is being taken care of" he continued, "and the Master asked that I come and tend to the gardens for a time."

Old man Chu's eyes looked me up and down where I stood, and then he stated. "I see you have grown. It looks as though you have stayed connected with the 1st Wisdom. I have heard of your journeys. It looks like it has taken some time for you to find your way. Tell me what have you returned from?"

I told old man Chu that I have returned from learning the 7th wisdom and told him about some of my exploits. I reviewed all the things I had learned, and explained how I had found the wisdom of relationship is what connects them all.

I told him that all the other wisdoms were connected to the relationships I had made. In life, our relationships are like gears that move us to the other wisdoms. To summarize the wisdom gained on my journey:

The First Wisdom – Physical

Physical is a relationship that your spirit has with your physical body. Without spirit and body being connected you cannot control your body or mind. Exercise and the good food you take in, is only part of the physical wisdom. Having a healthy relationship with your spiritual-self, drives the health of your physical body. When the soul is sad and in despair, the physical body follows and weakens.

The Second Wisdom – Learning

The full measure of learning in life can only be obtained with the connection of those in your life. You learn more with the assistance of others. The relationships in your life move your lesson from mere knowledge to wisdom. Our relationships teach us the broader truths in life. How we choose to see our relationships is how we choose to learn.

The Third Wisdom – Spiritual

Spiritual is your relationship with your spirit, and with the Great Spirit. And, contains the ability to connect to a deeper part of others. We all have a spiritual connection with each other and can feel that connection as we interact. A spiritual relationship is felt from the heart, such as the strong loving connection two people make in an instant, even though they have never seen each other. It is two souls remembering each other from a spiritual life not of this world.

The Fourth Wisdom – Service

Service is when we do action for those with whom we have relationships with, that our own life is blessed. It is the act of others filling an empty cup. To drink from the cup of service someone must be there to fill it. The power of service is the selflessness shown to others. An open and honest act of service is one of the most powerful relationship connections in this world. It gives us the opportunity to show our true love.

The Fifth Wisdom – Thoughts

As we see the good in people that is what they will become. I am always looking with gratitude at the relationships in my life. I am grateful for all who have come into my life to be my teachers. I live in the now, and connect with others in the moment, without holding on to old ills or false statements. As I see the good in the people I meet; they also see the good in me.

The Sixth Wisdom – Words

Words can destroy relationships, or build them. A word can create a feeling of love, or destroy a friendship. You may forgive someone for an act of betrayal, but you will never forget how it made you feel. Words are the poison, however can be the elixir of life. Words can destroy or create the connection between worlds. Be the good word, and the relationships in your life will be strong and everlasting.

The Seventh Wisdom – Relationships

Relationship is the Wisdom that connects all the other wisdoms together.

There is no wisdom without a connection to everything, and everyone, we interact with in our lives.

He seemed to listen, but as I was done talking he put his hand on his chin, then he looked up and said, "it is too bad you missed the most important part."

"What?" I thought.

"What do you mean" I asked?

"There is one person that you missed in your explanations about relationship that is the most important", he said.

Old man Chu's face softened as he continued, "My boy I know of the eight wisdoms and I know what you have been through to have come thus far." He looked at me with such compassion and love, and then he explained, "Your true and final test is still to come! If you don't comprehend the most important relationship in your life, I fear you may not overcome what is before you."

I was shaken by his sincerity and passion; something I had never seen from this person before. A shiver began to creep through my whole body. As Old man Chu continued to speak:

"You must have a strong relationship with yourself my boy! People connect with others, or say they love others, but if you don't truly understand yourself and have a strong connection with self, you will not be able to take on the powerful forces that can potentially set you off-course in your life. Being connected with self, and in tune with your spirit and body connection, can keep you grounded during the biggest storms of life. Being selfless is great and noble, but at the expense of your self can lead to destruction.

Thoughts of others are the thoughts you have of yourself, because you are the only person you know and connect with, in your mind." He pointed to his temple. "If you cannot connect your mind with your spirit you will always be misled. Your spirit is the real you. Your mind is the instrument you have been given, that can teach your spirit. You can either learn and move forward, or refuse to learn and fall into the abyss, thus losing the connection with spirit and mind forever! This is what happens when your spirit darkens and lays dormant; sometimes never to awaken until after death. Many people in the world live a dead life, and my son it is sad and lonely. I am an old and simple man, and I do live connected to my mind and spirit."

I was focused on his speech as he finished with, "Shinhon love yourself and you will not let the outside world trick you." And with that said, the great and powerful Chu outstretched his arms and hugged me with a soft, sincere loving embrace.

We talked for what seemed a long time, and it was good.

A servant came to the garden and informed me that the Master was back and wanted me to see him in the Great Hall. I gave old man Chu one last embrace and continued onward to find the last wisdom.

I found the Master in the great hall, engulfed in thought. He had a look of fatigue, as if it was burdensome to see me. I asked, "What is the matter,

Master? Are you well? Have I done something to offend you?"

He replied, "No, young Shinhon. Do not concern yourself." With that he sat back in his chair. I was feeling uncomfortable, as I had never seen him with such a troubled spirit.

"I heard of what happened in Chee. I am grateful that you were there to assist General Yosha. What have you learned about this wisdom, Shinhon?" he queried.

I talked to him of what I had learned, and also what I had discussed with Old man Chu.

He said, "It was good."

WISDOM 8

"Hatred paralyzes life; love releases it.
Hatred confuses life; love harmonizes it.
Hatred darkens life; love illuminates it."

DR. MARTIN LUTHER KING JR.

Between Love and Loathing

All I could think about was Aryia. I loved her to the point of a continual heartache. I was tempted to forget the last wisdom, but I also had a deep love and respect for the Master and for all that I had learned.

I stood alone with the Master contemplating the last wisdom. "I stand before you to learn the last great Wisdom. I have fallen in love and wish to marry the merchant Chinsha's daughter, Aryia. I am anxious to finish the last wisdom and live my life with her.

"Shinhon," he released a breath and looked at me with his piercing eyes. "The last wisdom is important and mastering of it can either destroy you or make you more than you ever thought possible. There is a prison to the north where Udoki resides. As you know he is the warlord responsible for killing your family and destroying your village."

My mind was trying to comprehend what the Master had just said. "What!" I yelled. The instant the words sank in, darkness filled my heart.

The Master had promised several years ago to assist me in capturing Udoki. Now he tells me that Udoki is in a prison waiting for me.

"Waiting, for me. I will kill him with my bare hands. I will wrap my hands around his throat and strangle him feeling a great victory as I watch him die. I am not a little boy anymore. He will look into my eyes and beg for mercy."

Then I wondered, how can a heart that was filled with love, instantly change to a dark heart filled with revenge? How powerful is hate? My mind filled with thoughts of destruction of the man called Udoki.

The Master spoke as he saw the rage in me. "For your last wisdom you are to go to the prison where you will stay with Udoki for ten days. And then you may do with him as you wish."

I thought, ten days. "Master, I cannot stand being with him for ten days, he must die as quickly as possible." I could feel the anger and hostility rushing through my entire body. My emotions changed from love to hate in one moment.

Then the Master spoke, "And so he shall Shinhon, but not for ten days after your arrival. I reiterate, you are to stay in the cell with him for the entire ten days. Know this, Shinhon, I love you and am proud of what you have accomplished, but if you kill Udoki before the tenth day, you will be banished from this land and never return."

"Why Master? There is no more that I can learn from this man? He cares nothing about the wisdoms, or honor, or sacrifice. He has taken my home, my family, and my childhood."

The Master's voice was stern as he repeated, "If he is dead before the ten days, you will be an outcast."

My mind flashed to Aryia. That meant I would not be able to get back to her.

"Master, I will do this last thing for you but, after this, I am free of my apprenticeship with you, is that correct? I have learned all the wisdoms and have assimilated them into my life, isn't that correct? I will always appreciate the opportunity I have had, but now I must be free."

The Master stated, "You have always been free, Shinhon, to choose with your own will, as you can now. You can kill the warrior before the ten days, if that is your choice. You can wait and do with him what you will, or leave now and never return. You make your own choice."

I have withstood many things. I have killed men, loved and assisted others, and learned from it all. I could do this.

"What is your choice, Shinhon?" the Master asked.

"I will do as you ask. I have lived my life dedicated to learn the wisdoms and I am grateful for all that has transpired. I shudder to think of my life without your guidance. I can do this thing."

The Master continued, "You will ride with the caravan to the prison. You have become quite a hero throughout the land. The people want you to lead the caravan feeling all will be safe with the great Shinhon."

"I will lead the caravan," was my reply. After preparations were made, I left with the caravan. This was to be a long trek and there were many city stops along the way. I was in a hurry to finish this deed and get back to Aryia.

It seemed that somehow every city knew of the caravan with the great Shinhon at the lead and we were given a generous welcome at every city with parties and parades. I had gained notoriety. It is strange that, in some way, I felt the Great Spirit had prepared me for this, to be an example, but I did not feel proud or even special, only that I was supposed to be. If they only knew of the darkness in my heart for the warlord. I did love the people and showed no malice. At times the hospitality of the city assisted me in forgetting Udoki and thoughts of the love I had for Aryia. I thought of the brother rulers of Ivicas and did my best to look at only the *now* and see good things, but the dark cloud that hung over me when I thought of that evil man, whom I swore to kill, kept saturating my mind. I wanted him dead.

I could feel the weight of my hatred grow the closer we got to the prison. Even those in the caravan could feel it. A dark energy hung over me and it was obvious that it affected everyone. After traveling many weeks we arrived at the prison and were welcomed. This was not just a prison, but a thriving metropolis.

I talked to the mayor of the city. I asked if he knew why I was here. He stated that he knew my reason and the warlord Udoki was waiting for me. I asked to be taken to his cell and start the countdown to the end of the ten days at once.

The mayor could see the darkness in my eyes and I knew it. I could tell that he believed it would be ten minutes and not the ten days allotted to me.

I was taken to the prison and led through many jail cells to a big dark cell in a corner. I wondered if that could be him lying there on the floor. He was not well. Just seeing him caused me to feel anger and rage and everything else was blotted out.

I remember fighting with the General Yosha. I remember my thoughts during battle.

"Survive and kill!"

This is what I was thinking now as my blood pumped through me like a waterfall.

I saw a man at the gate. I thought he must be the guard who was put there to watch me and witness the killing of Udoki. The guard looked familiar.

I asked, "Do I know you?" He was a gigantic man and it appeared to me that he looked like Makato, my friend who became my brother and died a great warrior's death. Udoki was a man who would not be privileged to experience a warrior's death.

"It is an honor to be in your presence," said the young man who looked like Makato. He was strong and he showed me great humility.

"Open the door," I said. He did as I asked and before I went in, the guard said, "He is an old and feeble man with very little life in him."

"And very little time either," I commented.

The door closed behind me—the door keeper had not taken my sword. I felt it burning my side as I walked over to where my greatest foe lay.

He rolled over. Our eyes locked; his eyes portrayed a sad, lost darkness of total despair, and my eyes were filled with hate and vengeance. My hand dropped to my sword. I grabbed it tightly and began to pull it out of the sheath.

The guard shouted at me and it sounded like it was the great voice of my long ago friend, Makato.

"Master, you have ten days."

'I could care less of the ten days, this rat would die now.'

Udoki closed his eyes no longer wanting to see my gaze, aware of what was next. I saw a tear falling down his check and his lips moved as I heard a soft sound.

"I am sorry," he whispered.

Sorry from this animal meant nothing to me, but at that instant, Aryia appeared in my mind.

"I do not want you to go; I fear you may not return to me. Please, Shinhon, do whatever you must to come back to me, I love you."

I wondered why she had been so frantic but now I knew. I knew that if I killed this man I would destroy any chance of being with her. All the wisdoms I had learned would be for naught, and I would come full circle back to my burning village, all my friends and family lying dead on the ground. My life since then flashed before me.

"Love"

This word came to me in a clear sound.

"Love"

As I thought of Aryia and my love for her, I discovered I could suppress the rage.

Udoki waited for the darkness that would end his life and, as the guard watched, my hand loosened on the handle.

I stepped back many times and felt myself hit the other side of the cell hard, and then I slid down the bars. There I sat with my hands in my face thinking of my love, my only, my Aryia.

"I will do anything to come back to you."

The old warrior spoke. "My entire being shakes with sorrow for the misery I have caused, and all the lives I have destroyed."

"Shut up animal!" I screamed. "Another word and I will slash your throat, I swear it!"

There was silence in the dark cell except for my sobs. Time seemed to stop. The world had stopped.

Meals were brought to the door.

Neither the old man nor I ate anything.

He looked sick and helpless. Maybe I would not have to kill him.

The rest of the day and night passed in dark silence. There was no talking, only the feeling of hatred which consumed me. Kill him, kill him now! Every time I felt hatred, the memory of Aryia's face would calm me.

Five days went by and the urge to kill this vicious man grew weaker and weaker.

On the sixth day, out of the silence, I heard a voice.

"May I speak?" the old warrior whispered so low I could barely hear what he said.

His voice did not make me want to kill him.

"Yes, you may speak, but do not think that my feelings will be affected by anything you have to say."

I was surprised at how determined the guard was, never leaving the door. He was a great strength to me and somehow I think he knew it.

Udoki began to tell me a story. It was about a young boy who was raised in a wonderful land. He spoke softly as he related the life of this boy, the son of a blacksmith. Not just a blacksmith, but the blacksmith to the emperor of this great land. The boy's father was well respected by all the people. The boy was raised in the palace.

He was raised with a good and happy life, a loving mother and a strong father. He talked of the boy's friends and the games they used to play. He had a special friend; a girl named, Layia. She was his best friend. He told stories of the mischief they caused, never too bad, but all the things that kids do for fun.

He talked throughout the night, stopping only long enough to sip on water. It was day seven.

It was hard to believe that he could talk of such sweet things. He continued the story, saying that as they grew up together they were always best friends. The boy learned his father's trade and he became a noble and well respected blacksmith.

There were wars in the land and men were needed to fight for the emperor. The young boy wanted to be a soldier and protect the land he loved.

He told of the boy who became a soldier. He had seen battles and death and had fought with great honor and lost good friends.

'What do you know of friends?' I thought.

It was now day eight.

As he continued his story he told of the boy returning home, still very young, but old in spirit because of what he had seen and done. He had become a respected soldier. He returned home to take up his father's trade.

When he returned, Layia came to see her old friend and they were instantly in love. The young man was content with his love for Layia. They soon married and moved to a small city where he became the blacksmith. He was happier than he had ever been and felt he had it all, since their love was blossoming with a child on the way. The man loved to see his beautiful wife full with child. The recollections of war washed from his memory. While he told this story, he would falter many times as he spoke of Layia. I could not see him in the dark but thought maybe he was crying.

Then he said, "They came without warning. There was no time at all for anyone to fight the raiders. I heard the yelling of the guards and the ringing of the alarm bell. I ran from my shop."

Did he say "I?"

"Layia and I ran into the street. She was beautiful, filled with child. I saw a look of horror on her face. I turned and saw men coming fast on galloping horses, battle lust in their eyes. I saw the leader—you can always tell the leader. He had the bloodlust. I swung my sword but the horses were on both me and my Layia.

I only remember awaking after it was all over and the horror I felt when I saw my beautiful Layia trampled by the horses. I was beyond hurt and barely conscious, but I stared in disbelief at her lifeless body, still round with child."

Udoki was sobbing. I could barely understand his words as he relived this tale of misery and pain. I thought of my Aryia and tears flowed down my face. I knew the love this man had for his woman and I felt a crushing blow to my heart.

He continued, "I lived but swore vengeance on the warrior, his face burning deep into my consciousness. I would do anything to get revenge. I traveled a long distance and somehow was led to a great man in a faraway land. He was the Master, my strong and wise mentor. I asked him if he would help me find a way to destroy this warlord. He said he would but that I must learn the Wisdoms of Life. I accepted.

Udoki told of the many things he had learned in life and what the wisdoms meant to him.

"Shinhon," he said.

"Yes, Udoki." I replied.

"I learned many things in this life. I obtained knowledge but I also felt a bitter and vengeful hatred, and was blinded by it. I wanted people to know the pain of the loss I had suffered. There was nothing in my heart but retribution, as I blamed the world for my suffering. But, knowledge is the false prize of life. There are many knowledgeable people in the world, Shinhon, but without the wisdom to use knowledge wisely it is worth nothing.

"When I progressed to the last wisdom the Master told me of the warrior and that he had been found."

I could not believe my ears. "The Master gave me the same command that he gave you. Ten days, just ten days."

"I rushed into the cell of the warrior and it was over in seconds; the one who destroyed my life and family lay dead. One second was all it took. I lost more than just banishment from this land. I lost my soul. Even my heart turned cold. The only thing that fed me was absolute defeat, total conquest, and battle after battle. I would destroy anything in my path, secretly hoping that I would be killed. "I remember your village, I remember it well. It was a small village where we stopped to take supplies. The people of the village resisted."

Udoki paused for a moment to catch his breath. "I looked into your eyes that day, Shinhon, and I remembered myself standing beside my Layia and then lying there beside her; my world gone. I could see in your eyes the pain you felt, and knew that someday you would kill me just as I killed the man who took my wife.

He stopped again.

"I lost all desire to live. I traveled alone and was in hiding for many years in the waste lands. I found myself years later hearing the tales of the great Shinhon. I went to the palace door of the Master and asked to be your last wisdom. I knew it had to be me. The Master had me placed in prison until now."

It was past day nine.

I felt something stir deep inside me. I knew that at one time this man was full of hope, love, and excitement for life. But it had been stolen from him, as mine was stolen from me. Something in my own heart gave way. I sat beside the man. I had not noticed how ill he was.

"Master Udoki," I said.

He looked at me with tears streaming down his face. I have decided I will not kill you. I will let you free. It is my choice.

He said softly, "I often thought of the child in my Layia's belly and thought of how it would be to have a son. I would wish him to be like you."

I was one with his pain and could feel empathy for the love of his Layia and baby.

Udoki, I will take you back to the Master and pronounce that from here after you have a son.

In a weak voice he whispered, "I cannot go. But there is one thing. Will you forgive me?"

I leaned down and kissed the forehead of the man, my ultimate teacher and as I leaned over saying "Yes, I forgive you." Aryia's necklace hung down between us.

Udoki the warrior, loving husband and father raised his hand to four. I did as well. We embraced as father and son. I felt Udoki's last breath.

It was day ten and the great Udoki was dead— but not at my hand. The guard was gone. Why would he go? I wanted to tell him thank you and that I wished for an honorable soldier's burning for Udoki. I sat with Udoki for some time.

The mayor along with some others entered the door of the cell. "It has

259

been ten days," the mayor exclaimed.

I looked at the mayor with my arms around Udoki and said, "Yes, the great Udoki is dead, but not at my hand."

I stood up asking the mayor, "Where is the man that has been here guarding the door? I wish to thank him."

"What man?" The mayor asked puzzled. "We were instructed to leave you alone except for delivering food and drink."

There appeared a smile of realization on my face.

I told the mayor to prepare a great bonfire because this would be the funeral of a great soldier and a celebration of a good man.

The mayor did as I asked. The bonfire was large and my greatest teacher, Udoki, was placed on the burning pyre. The flames consumed his body. As it burned a realization came over me. I was not the same man I once was. Sadness and darkness lifted. I felt a new power. I was at one with all eight wisdoms of life. I was whole.

It wasn't about learning, or knowledge of the eight Wisdoms. The only way to connect with them was by being them. They were now me.

On the ground in front of the bonfire and as the great Udoki was consumed by the flames, I wrote the 8 Wisdoms on my parchment journal. With time in the temple, I had learned of writing numbers and symbols, and as I gazed at the number 8 I realized something, the 8 was a symbol of something else.

On its side it was the symbol for infinity:

To master the 8 Wisdoms was to have infinite Wisdom.

I would go and marry Aryia, returning to let the Master know that I was now connected with all eight Wisdoms.

There was a new caravan traveling back to Hiin. I was given the opportunity to lead this caravan. The trip back was different from the one before. I felt so much love in my heart. When we stopped at cities, I was loving, loved, and excited for life. The world was shining with a brightness I had never witnessed before.

Love. There was no greater wisdom than Love.

My heart pounded harder and harder as I got closer to my Aryia. I could feel her presence as I came closer. My love for her was greater than ever. I was a part of the world and Aryia was a part of me. There was magic in the world.

There was my love in front of her home. I stood and looked at her. She looked up and saw me. She ran to me and wrapped her arms around me. I could hear her soft sobs of relief.

"You came back to me," she whispered.

She raised her head from my chest and looked into my eyes. We both shed tears as we kissed. "I promised you I would come back."

"Do you remember me?" she said with a smile. I smiled at her. "You are the most beautiful thing in the world and I will never forget you. You are everything to me. You are the part that makes me whole. You will always be the light of my day and the air that I breathe. Aryia, I love you and my only wish is always to be with you."

Aryia asked through her tear-filled eyes, "Did you finish the last wisdom?"

"Yes I did," I replied.

"Was it difficult?" she asked.

I smiled at her, kissed her on the cheek and said, "It was the most important."

She looked at me saying, "I feel there is something different about you."

"Yes, I am whole and wish only to be your husband, if you will have me."

She buried her head in my chest. "Yes, yes!" She replied, "I wish for nothing else."

We made arrangements for the ceremony with the great merchant, Chinsha. There was a celebration in the streets. After the ceremony and the celebration I told Chinsha that I was going to take his daughter, now my wife, to see the Master. We left on horseback and arrived at the great palace early in the day.

As we rode to the gates I thought of how the guards bowed to me with great respect. I had done this so many times before entering the gates. I remembered that first time some years ago. I was a hopeless lost boy.

"Master Shinhon, it is good to see you," said the lead guard. I was now welcomed as if it were my own palace. We put the horses in the stables and left for the palace.

I found Mehi, hugged her, and introduced her to my new wife. She was overjoyed for us. I asked where the Master was. She told me he was in the main garden. I asked Mehi to show Aryia around and I would visit the Master. I found him in the garden, deep in thought.

He looked up at me with a smile on his face. "Shinhon," he stood and asked me to join him. "I see that you have learned the last wisdom. Your countenance has changed. You are not the person who left this palace."

I told him about what had happened in the prison and that I knew Udoki was his apprentice at one time. As I let go of my hate and anger, the world changed. I told him of my new wife, who was in the palace with me, and the strong love that we had for each other. He was excited to meet her.

As we walked in the garden the Master asked me. "What is the last wisdom?"

"Love, Master the last wisdom is love. Love is the purest of all of the Wisdoms. Not only is it a pure Wisdom, but. . ." I knelt to the ground and with my finger drew six circles. In each circle I wrote a word.

Physical

Thought   Words

Spiritual   Service

Learning

I then connected them with a circle. "You see the first six are necessary but the Seventh Wisdom of relationships connects them all. I wrote the word relationship in the middle of the big circle.

Then I drew another circle around them all.

This is love. Above it I wrote the word, <u>Love</u>.

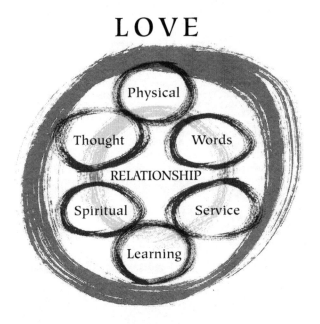

I pointed to each word and explained them all.

Physical – You must love yourself and treat your body well.

Learning – You must love to learn or you will not learn.

Spiritual – The love of your spirit and others connect you with the Great Spirit and the entire universe.

Service – You must love others to give true service.

Words – The word is Love and if you are true to that word all others spoken will be for good.

Thought – Thoughts of love will always take you to a better place and gratitude for the love in your life will always present you with light.

Relationships – As long as there is love in relationships we will never be alone and all other wisdoms will connect.

As I finished my summary of the connection of love with the other wisdoms I continued to speak, "As we all live the wisdoms we will be infinitely more valuable to the world, to ourselves, and to those around us."

The Master looked at me and pulled something from under his garment.

It was a medallion that hung around his neck. Six circles connected by one big circle. Surrounding them all was an even larger circle and in the middle an eight-pointed star.

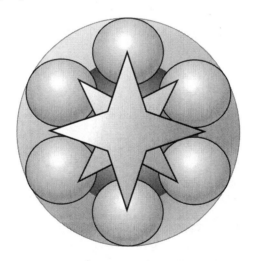

As he held the medallion up and let it drop back down, he said, "There is one last thing you must know. The one thing that will keep the fire of the wisdoms in your life is accountability. The star on this medallion represents accountability and it is what connects you to living the wisdoms. You are accountable for yourself and the choices you make in life. Who you are is because of the choices you have made. The accountability of the Eight Wisdoms in your life is what makes you the master or, the slave. When accountability is forgotten all of the wisdoms fall away.

"Udoki neglected his accountability. It is never about the other person when it comes to your own responsibility. Udoki's choice was to use his hatred of one man to justify his actions. You could have killed Udoki the second you saw him but you did not."

I interrupted the Master and said, "but Master, if Aryia had not been in my thoughts I would have surely killed Udoki.

He smiled, "Yes, but it was you who made it possible by permitting her love to influence your heart. Wisdom holds you accountable for yourself, and how you live the wisdoms is something that only you can control."

The Master put his hand to his heart and said, "The Wisdom of Love is the most powerful force on earth. If you do not hold yourself accountable for how and who you love, the Wisdom of Love is lost.

He then pointed to me and back at himself saying, "Relationships with the world and people in it move our reality. If you do not accept accountability for the relationships in your life, all relationships are lost or shallow."

The Master then pointed to his mouth, "Words create or destroy. If you are not accountable for the words you use, you can never heal the damage you have caused or bask in the joy you have created."

He pointed a finger to the temple of his head, "Thoughts are the driving force of the directions in our life. If you do not take accountability for your own thoughts, your life will be chaos."

The Master opened his arms as if to embrace someone, "Service is love focused outward. If you cannot account for the charity you show others, your heart will never be complete, only filled with an emptiness and regret.

He then put his hands together and placed the connected hands in front of his face. "Your spirit is the ultimate guide. If you do not take accountability for your own spirituality, you will never have the guidance of spirit."

The Master then bent to the ground and wrote the word *learn* in the dirt. "Learning is what keeps us alive and is the reason for our existence. If you are not accountable for what you learn then you will be lead blindly down a path going nowhere."

The Master picked a beautiful blue flower from a bush beside us and said, "The physical world is all around us and that includes this physical body that houses our spiritual energy. If you do not take accountability for your body, your mind and body will fail you."

I bowed my head to the Master and said, "Thank you for the gifts you have given me. The connections I have with the wisdoms will forever be a part of me and I humble myself before you as my master, my mentor, my teacher, and my friend."

The Master spoke in a soft loving voice. "You are no longer the apprentice, Shinhon, you have grown from a boy, but you are more than a man. You are now The Master!"